The Boy With the U.S. Miners

Francis Rolt-Wheeler

THE BOY WITH THE U S. MINERS

CHAPTER I

UNDERGROUND TERRORS

"Ay, lad," said the old miner, the pale flame of his cap-lamp lighting up his wrinkled face and throwing a distorted shadow on the wall of coal behind, "there's goin' to be a plenty of us killed soon."

"Likely enough, if they're all as careless as you," Clem retorted.

"Carelessness ain't got nothin' to do with it," the old man replied. "The 'knockers' has got to be satisfied! There ain't been an accident here for months. It'll come soon! The spirits o' the mine is gettin' hungry for blood."

"Nonsense, Otto! The idea of an old-timer like you believing in goblins and all that superstitious stuff!"

"It's easy enough for you to say 'nonsense,' Clem Swinton, an' to make game o' men who were handlin' a coal pick when you was playin' with a rattle, but that don't change the facts. Why, even Anton, here, youngster that he is, knows better'n to deny the spirits below ground. The knockers got your father, Anton, didn't they?"

Anton Rover, one of the youngest boys in the mine, to whom the old miner had turned for affirmation, nodded his head in agreement. Like many of his fellows, the lad was profoundly credulous.

From his Polish mother — herself the daughter of a Polish miner — Anton had inherited a firm belief in demons, goblins, gnomes, trolls, kobolds, knockers, and the various races of weird creatures with which the Slavic and Teutonic peoples have dowered the world underground. From his earliest childhood he had been familiar with tales of subterranean terror, and he knew that his father had often foregone a day's work and a day's pay rather than go down the mine-shaft if some evil omen had occurred.

Yet Anton was willing to accept modern ideas, also. Clem was both his protector and his chum, and the boy had a great respect for his older comrade's knowledge and good sense. He was aware, too, that Clem was unusually well informed, for the young fellow was a natural student and was fitting himself for a higher position in the mine by hard reading. This Ohio mine, like many of the American collieries, maintained a free school and an admirable technical library for the use of those workers who wished to better themselves.

The young student miner was zealous in his efforts to promote modern ideas among his comrades, and knew that the old superstitions bred carelessness and a blind belief in Fate. Despite their differences in age and in points of view, he and Otto were warm friends, and he returned the old man's attack promptly.

"So far as Anton's father is concerned, Otto," he said, "it was Jim Rover's carelessness that killed him. He was caught by a falling roof just because he wouldn't take the trouble to make sure that the draw slate overhead was solid before setting to work to undercut the coal. I know that's so, because he told me, just before he died. I was the first one to reach him, after the fall, for I was working in the next room, just around the rib."

"An' who made the draw slate fall, just when Jim Rover was a-standin' right under it? Answer me that, Clem Swinton!"

The other shrugged his shoulders.

"Every man who's ever handled a coal pick knows that draw slate is apt to work loose. That's one of the dangers of the business. And the danger can be avoided, as you know perfectly well, Otto, if a chap will feel the roof for vibration, with one hand, while he uses the other to tap on the slate with the flat side of a pick. If he won't take the trouble — why, it's his own fault if he gets killed.

"Blaming the 'knockers,' Otto, doesn't hide the fact that nearly a thousand miners get killed in the United States every year, just through their own carelessness."

The old man shook a finger ominously.

"It isn't always the careless ones what get taken," he declared. "Look out for yourself, Clem Swinton; look out for yourself! It's you the knockers'll be after, next, an' much good all your readin'll do you, then! I warned Jim Rover less'n a week afore he got killed, an' I'm warnin' you now."

Anton looked up, fearfully, for old Otto had a reputation as a seer, in the mine, but Clem only laughed.

"I put my faith in following out the safety rules, Otto," he replied, "not in charms and tricks to keep the goblins away."

The old man, however, was not thus to be set aside. He was as ready to defend his old-fashioned beliefs as was Clem to advance his modern theories.

"Experience goes for somethin'," he affirmed stubbornly. "Boy an' man, I've been below ground for over forty years. I've worked in Germany, Belgium, France, and all over this country. Just eight years old I was, when I went down the shaft for the first time; there weren't no laws, then, to keep youngsters out of a mine.

"I was a door-boy to start off with, openin' doors for the coal-cars to come through. That meant keeping one's ears open. The loaded cars come a-roarin' down the slopin' galleries, an', if a kid didn't hear them, he'd get smashed between the coal car an' the door. Even when he did hear them, he had to jump lively, or he'd get nipped, anyhow.

"On the other side o' the door it wasn't much better, for the empty cars were hauled up the slope o' the mine galleries by donkey power, an', if a kid didn't hear the whistle o' the donkey driver, he'd get his head clouted an' would be fined two days' pay beside.

"There warn't no eight-hours' day, then. We worked a shift o' twelve hours, an' the miners didn't stop between for meals — just took their grub in bites while they went on holin' coal. All piece-work it was in them days, an' every miner holed, spragged (or timbered), picked and loaded his own coal. The more stuff he got out, the more pay. The men didn't get any too much money, either, an' if a miner wanted to have a decent pay-check at the end o' the week, he warn't goin' to be hindered by havin' any trouble with cars. The poor kid at the door got it comin' to him from all sides.

"It's different now in coal-mines to what it was then. We hadn't no electric plant to run ventilatin' fans for keepin' the air fit to breathe. Nowadays, a

4

man can be nigh as comfortable below ground as he can be above; but, when I was a kid, the air in a mine was hot, an' heavy, an' sleepy-like.

"After breathin' that air for nine or ten hours, it was hard to keep awake. You'd see the pit-boys comin' up out o' the shaft wi' their eyes all red an' swollen an' achin'. No, it warn't from gas, it was just from rubbin' em to keep em' open. An' rubbin' your eyes with hands all gritty with coal-dust ain't any too good for 'em."

"Well, Otto," the young fellow interrupted, "you can't deny that modern methods have improved all that. There aren't any door-boys in a modern mine. Most of the States in this country have passed laws requiring that all doors through which coal cars pass must be operated automatically. The United States Bureau of Mines keeps a sharp lookout, too. There aren't any donkeys, either, not in up-to-date mines; endless-chain conveyors take the coal from the face where the miner has dug it clear to the mouth of the shaft, and load it into the buckets by a self-tipping device. As for small boys in a mine, as you said yourself, there aren't any, not in the United States, anyhow."

"I'm not denyin' that minin' has got easier," was the grudging reply, "it'd be a wonder if it hadn't. What I'm sayin' is that all your newfangled schemes don't stop accidents and won't never stop accidents, not till you get rid o' the knockers an' gas sprites of a mine. An' that you'll never do!

"You're like a whole lot o' these young fellows, Clem, who believe nothin' that they don't see. You don't never stop to think that maybe it's your own blindness an' not your own cleverness that keeps you from seem'. Wait till I tell you what happened to me, one time, when I was a door-boy in Germany.

"Long afore I first went down into a coal mine, I knew about the knockers, and where they come from. Dad told me that all the coal-seams o' the world were forests, once. Long afore Noah an' the Flood. He'd seen ferns an' leaves o' trees turned into coal. One time, when digging out a seam, he'd come across the trunk of a tree standin' upright in the coal, with the roots still in the under clay."

"That's right enough," agreed Clem, "but the coal-forests were a good many million years older than Noah!"

"Maybe, maybe; but you warn't there to see," Otto retorted. "Anyhow, there were forests, an' these forests were standin' afore the Flood. Judgin' by what's left, the trees o' these forests must ha' been big.

"All those trees, Dad used to say, had spirits o' their own, just like trees have to-day. Elves an' dryads, he used to call 'em. When the Flood came an' spread deep water over the whole world, the tops o' the hills were washed into the valleys an' all these forests were covered in mud an' sand. That's how it is you never find anything but shale or slate (which is mud-rock) or sandstone above a coal seam. What's more, when pullin' down slate, you'll often find sea-shells, like mussels an' clams. Ain't that so?"

"I won't argue with you about the Flood, Otto, for that's a long story. But you're dead right in saying that all coal seams are overlaid with rocks which have been laid down by water, and that fossil shells are found in the overlying layers. But go ahead and tell us what you saw."

"When the Flood came," the old man resumed, "the elves an' dryads what used to live in the coal-trees were swallowed up in the water. They weren't drowned, because spirits can't die—at least, that was what Dad told me. They couldn't go away from their trees, because the trees were still standin' there, though all covered in mud or sand. So they had to change their ways for a new life, first under the water, an' when the waters o' the Flood dried up, under the ground. The elves, who were the men-spirits o' the forest, became knockers; the dryads, who were the women-spirits o' the trees, became the sprites o' the gas damps.

"In the old days, folks used to be able to see these spirits o' the forests. They used to build temples to 'em, an' have regular festivals in the woods, always leavin' some food for 'em to eat. Dad told me never to forget that the only way to keep on the good side o' the spirits below ground was to keep out o' the mine on the first day o' spring an' the last day o' summer, an' every time I took anything to eat below ground, to leave a bite behind.

"I've always done it. In all the years I've been minin', I've never gone down the shaft on March 21st or September 20th, an' I never will. An', every time I've taken my dinner-pail to the face where I was workin', I've put a bit o' bread aside for the knockers. You can believe it or not, as you like, but when I got back to the place, on my next shift, the bread was gone."

"Probably rats," commented Clem, in an aside to Anton.

The old miner paid no heed to the interruption, if, indeed, he heard it.

"That way, I always knew that the knockers were on my side, an' I've been willin' to hole coal in mines that folks said weren't safe. What's more, in forty years o' work, I've never lost a day's time from an accident of any kind. I know I'm safe, because of what happened to me when I was still a kid.

"One day — I don't know just why, maybe the air was worse'n usual — after I'd been lookin' after the door for the bigger part o' the shift, I dropped right off asleep. Half-dreamin', I heard a loaded car come roarin' down, but I didn't wake up until it was so close as to be too late.

"I scrambled up on my feet an' was just makin' a wild jump forward to the door, when I felt a little fist — it seemed about the size of a baby's, but was strong an' hard — hit me right in the chest. It pushed me back into the corner, out o' the way o' the car, an' held me there.

"At the same minute, an' just in the nick o' time, the door swung open.

"Rubbin' my eyes — they was so gritty wi' coal that I could hardly look out o' them — I saw what looked like a little man made o' coal standin' back against the door an' holdin' it open for the car to pass through. His face was sort o' pale, like a whitewashed wall in the dark, an' his eyes were red, like sparks. I thought he had a pointed hat an' long pointed shoes, but I was so scared that I couldn't be rightly sure. I could just see his whitish face movin' up an' down, like he was noddin' his head. Then the door slammed shut, the hand suddenly lifted off my chest an' I didn't see nothin' more. I tell you, I kept awake after that."

"You must have opened the door unconsciously, while half-asleep, and dreamed about seeing the goblin," was Clem's comment.

7

But, before the old man could retort, Anton broke in.

"Father told me he's seen some, just like that. It was in Wales. A woman visitor had gone down to see the mine."

Otto shook his head gravely.

"Never a woman went down a coal mine yet, but an accident happened right after," he declared. "In the big explosion at Loosburg, when over four hundred miners were killed, it was found out, after, that one o' the miners was a woman who had dressed herself in men's clothes an' was pickin' coal. But what was it your father saw, Anton?"

"It happened right when the visiting party was in the mine," the boy explained. "It was in one of the main galleries, which was strongly timbered. A prop, which had been standing firmly for ever so many years, suddenly crumbled into splinters and the roof fell on the woman, hurting her so badly that she died soon after she was taken to the top.

"Just after the roof fell, so Father said, he and all the rest of the miners saw a band of knockers gathered around the pile of fallen roof and pointing at the figure of the woman crushed beneath. He said the knockers were laughing so loudly that some of the miners heard the echoes away at the other end of the mine."

"And do you believe that, Anton?" queried Clem, incredulously.

"Father saw them himself," the boy replied, in a tone of finality.

"Then there's the gas sprites," Otto went on, pleased at having found a sympathetic listener. "I've never seen 'em myself, but there's plenty that have. In a mine where I used to work, in Belgium, there was a man who could see 'em as plain as I see you or Anton. That was his job, and he was paid handsomely, too.

"He could walk through a gallery, either in a workin' or an abandoned mine, an' could tell right away if there was fire damp, or white damp, or black damp, or stink damp, in the workin's. He could see the gas sprites himself an' give warnin' where men had better not go. He didn't have to carry a safety lamp, nor chemical apparatus, nor cages of mice an' canaries, the way folks do, now. He just walked into the mine an' saw the sprites. He was friendly to 'em, an' they never did him no harm."

"What were they like, Otto?" queried Anton.

"Shadows o' women," the old man replied promptly. "Fire damp, this diviner used to say, looked like a figure veiled in red, black damp was veiled in black wi' white edges, white damp was bluish, an' stink damp was yellow. When the gas was faint, all he could see was just the glow o' the colors, very dim; but when the gas was strong then the shapes o' the women were bold an' clear.

"The gas sprites, bein' women, catch an' hold the young men an' the single men more easily than old an' married miners. You don't deny that single men are more often killed by damps than married men, do you, Clem?"

The young miner looked uncomfortable at the question.

"That's a general belief, and statistics seem to back it up," he admitted. "But I don't see that it has anything to do with your goblin ideas, Otto. It's just because the single men, generally, are the youngest, and they haven't become as immune to the poisonous gases of the mine as men who have been working below ground all their lives."

"You can explain away anything, if you have a mind to," Otto retorted scornfully. "But as long as men are workin' below ground, there's goin' to be knockers an' sprites o' the damps, an' miners is goin' to be killed. Me, I've escaped. Why? Because I'm chock-full o' science an' modern ideas? Not a bit of it! I get along because I know what the spirits o' the mine expect, an' I give it to 'em. Right now, I'm the oldest man at work, here, an' I ain't never had an accident."

"Don't you believe his stories, Anton," the young miner protested, turning to the boy. "Those antiquated notions will only lead you astray. The 'damps' are just various kinds of gases coming out of the coal, and the way to fight them is to keep a strong current of air going through the mine."

"How do they come out o' the coal, if you know so much?" questioned Otto, belligerently.

"Sure I know! But I don't suppose telling you will change your ideas."

"It won't," the old miner admitted frankly. "But I've had my say, an' it's only fair to let you have yours. The youngster, here, can believe which o' the two he pleases."

"Well, it's something this way," Clem began, casting about in his mind for a way to explain the chemistry of mine air as simply as he could. "Ordinary air — the air above ground — is made up of a little less than 21 per cent. of oxygen and a little more than 78 per cent. of nitrogen. The rest of it is a mixture of carbon and oxygen which the books call carbon dioxide or black damp, with some other rare gases beside.

"Now, all animals, including man, depend for their life on the oxygen in the air. If the oxygen drops to 15 per cent., a man will suffer. That's not likely to happen where miners' lamps or safety-lamps are used, because the flame of a lamp goes out when there's less than 17 per cent. oxygen. Even at 19 per cent., a lamp will burn so dimly as to warn of danger. The nitrogen in the air is inert, that is, it does neither good nor harm to man. But what I want you to remember, Anton, is that even in the purest air above ground, there's always some 'black damp,' so it's a bit hard to see where Otto's goblin women come in!

"Now, when pure air comes down a coal shaft, a lot of changes happen to it. Some of the oxygen is consumed by the breathing of the men and animals in the mine — if there are any donkeys or such — some is taken up by the burning of lamps, some more by the explosion of blasting powder, a little is lost by the rusting of iron pyrites — which is found in many coal mines — and a lot of it is taken up by the coal, just how, we don't quite know."

"It's good to hear o' somethin' you don't know," the old miner remarked sarcastically. "But you're talkin' about dry air, an' the air in most mines is moist."

"Quite right," Clem agreed. "It has to be. Mine air is made moist, on purpose, especially in winter."

"It is?" Otto's voice expressed unqualified astonishment.

"It certainly is! In most coal-mines — this one, for instance — all the air that passes down the intake shaft is moistened by a spray of mixed water and air, so finely atomized that it floats like a cloud."

"What for? It's easier to work in dry air'n moist air."

"It's easier to get blown up, too! In winter time, Otto, the air above ground is a lot colder than the air in the mine. Cold air can't hold as much moisture as warm air, and as soon as air gets warmed up a bit, it tries its hardest to absorb any moisture with which it happens to come in contact.

"What happens in a mine, in such a case? Why, as the cold air from above passes through the galleries of a mine, it gets warmed up. As it warms up, it draws out from the roofs, the ribs, and the floors all the water that there is to draw, and makes the mine dead dry. When coal dust is absolutely dry, it crumbles into finer and finer dust, until at last the particles are so small that they float in the air. Then comes disaster, for finely divided coal dust is so explosive that the smallest flame — even a spark from the stroke of a pick — will set the whole mine ablaze."

"I don't see that," interrupted Anton. "If dust is so bad, why do the bosses hang boards from all the gallery roofs and pile them high with dust?"

"Because the dust in those piles is stone dust, my boy," the young fellow explained. "When an explosion happens, it drives a big blast of air in front of it, so strong, sometimes, as to knock a man down. The blast of air blows all the stone dust from those boards and fills the air chock-full of it.

"This stone dust, usually made from crushed limestone or crushed shale, won't burn. The flame of the explosion can't pass through and the fire can't jump a rock-dust barrier. Even the flame of methane, which you know better as 'gas,' or fire damp, which has a terrific force, is choked back by this dense cloud of rock-dust, and, as you know, all coal mines have more or less methane gas."

"They don't, either," contradicted Otto. "I've worked in mines for years at a time an' never seen the 'cap' on the flame of the safety-lamp, tellin' there's fire damp there."

"You may not have seen it, but there was gas there, just the same. As for the cap-flame you're talking about, Otto, I'll admit that it's the surest way of telling when there's so much fire-damp that the mine is getting dangerous. But it's a risky test, just the same. You can't see the little cap of methane gas flame burning above the oil flame of the lamp until there's 2 per cent. of gas in the air of the mine, and a little more than 5 per cent. will start an explosion."

"What makes that cap?" queried Anton.

"Fire damp or methane gas burning inside the wire gauze of the safety-lamp."

"But if the gas is already burning inside, why doesn't it explode outside?"

"Just because it's a safety-lamp, my boy. That's why the flame burns inside a wire gauze. I'll explain that.

"Suppose you take a lamp with a hot flame — an alcohol or spirit lamp will do — and light it. Then hold a piece of close-meshed wire gauze right on the flame. You'll find that the flame will spread under the wire gauze but will not go through. Hold it long enough, though, until the wire gets red hot, and, quite suddenly, the flame will pass through and burn above the gauze as well as below.

"Try another trick. Put out the lamp and then hold the gauze just where it was before. You can light the flame above the wire but it will not pass below the gauze until the wire gets red-hot. That shows that gas which is not burning can pass through a wire gauze, but that gas which is aflame cannot pass until the wire is red-hot."

"Yes," said Anton, "I can see that."

"Very good. Then, if you have a lamp which is burning inside a cylinder of wire gauze, the gas of fire-damp can go through, and, if there's enough of it to burn, it will burn above the flame of the lamp, making an aureole or 'cap' just as Otto says. But the flaming gas can't get back through the wire gauze to set fire to the fire-damp outside, at least, not until the wire gets red-hot, which it's not likely to do, seeing that the gas is in the middle, not underneath it.

"That's how they test for fire-damp, nowadays. The flame of a safety-lamp is drawn down until it shows only a small yellow tip. If there's any fire-damp in the air, a light-blue halo appears over the yellow flame. At a little more than 1 per cent., an experienced man can judge that there is gas there, but the true 'cap,' which is pointed like a cone, doesn't show until there's 2 per cent. of the gas. At 3 per cent., the cap will be like a dunce's cap, and more than half an inch high. At 4 per cent., it will be over an inch high, and at 4-1/2 per cent. it'll form a column of blue flame. Then it's high time to get out of the mine, and to get out quickly.

"In the improved form of safety-lamps, the oil flame burns inside a glass, but the air which reaches the flame has to pass through two cylinders of wire gauze. The glass keeps the flame from ever touching the innermost gauze, and, if an accident happens — such as the breaking of the glass — it would still be fairly safe, for the burning gas inside wouldn't pass through the inner gauze until that got red-hot, and it wouldn't reach the outer gauze because the current of air passing down between the two layers of wire mesh would keep the outer gauze cool. This safety-lamp was invented by Sir Humphry Davy, in England, in 1815, just after a big explosion in an English colliery had cost hundreds of lives. All mines nowadays require that miners use either safety-lamps or electric lamps, and it's every miner's business to report to the boss when he sees a cap of burning gas inside his safety-lamp."

The old miner nodded his head in agreement.

"I won't use an electric lamp," he commented. "It's foolishness. The gas sprites ain't really malicious. They're willin' enough to give a warnin'. They'll put a cap on a flame if they don't want folks in that part of the mine. An electric lamp tells nothin'. It won't even give a warnin' against black damp."

"Perfectly true," Clem agreed. "With an oil safety-lamp, the flame gets dim or even goes out if there's too much black damp. The electric lamp burns on, just the same, because the light is in a vacuum. Black damp isn't so dangerous as fire damp, though. It only causes distress and hard breathing because it shows that there's too big a proportion of nitrogen and carbon dioxide in the air and not enough oxygen. It's oxygen that a man misses."

"But black damp'll explode, too," put in Otto.

"No," the other corrected, "it won't. But it often happens that there's fire-damp around when black damp is present and the black damp makes a test for gas difficult. It's the gas that explodes, not the black damp.

"It isn't always the explosiveness of a damp that makes it dangerous, though," he went on. "As Otto could tell you, Anton, white damp is the worst of the three. And it doesn't give any warning at all."

"That's why we had that diviner in a Belgian mine," the old man commented, gravely. "He could see the gas sprites in their blue veils. But, if there's a lot o' white damp, you can tell it by the flame of a safety-lamp gettin' a little longer an' brighter."

"It's not safe to trust it," the young fellow advised. "You'd have trouble seeing 2 per cent, of white damp, and you'd be dead before you had much chance to look. Even with 1-1/2 per cent., a man would be likely to drop before he reached a better-ventilated part of the mine, and he couldn't see that much on the flame of his safety-lamp at all. To breathe the air with only 1 per cent. of white damp for an hour would put a man in such a state that he mightn't recover, and he wouldn't have had any warning.

"Luckily, there's much less danger of white damp in mines than there used to be. It's a gas that's formed only when there's been something burning. After an explosion in a mine, or a fire, there's sure to be a lot of it, and rescue parties have always found it their worst foe. But, in the ordinary working mine, it is rare."

"Not so rare as all that!" objected Otto. "We used to have a lot of it, on the other side."

"You wouldn't now," was the reply. "The white damp of those days was due to the heavy charges of gunpowder or low explosive that were used, explosives which are forbidden now in dangerous mines."

"They were better'n the stuff we use nowadays," grumbled Otto, "they brought down more coal an' didn't smash it up so bad."

"They smashed up men, instead," Clem retorted. "And they put a whole lot of white damp into a mine. That was really dangerous, because, in those days, people hadn't found out the value of canaries."

"I've often wondered about that," interjected Anton. "Why do the testing-parties carry canaries?"

"Because," answered Clem, with a smile, "canaries are as clever at seeing the gas sprites as was the Belgian diviner that Otto talks about. No, but seriously," he went on, "the reason is that canaries are extremely susceptible to white damp. Less than 1/4 of one per cent of white damp will cause a canary to collapse at once, and a man could breath that proportion for an hour without much harm. Even a tenth of one per cent. will cause the little bird to show signs of distress."

"It's tough on the bird," was Anton's sympathetic comment.

"Not especially! As soon as a bird begins to show collapse, it is taken back to the open air and is as frisky and lively as ever in five minutes. But its value as a warning signal is enormous, for it tells rescue parties or investigating parties when to put on gas masks or breathing apparatus containing oxygen. In a well-ventilated mine, however, where high explosive is used and handled by experienced men, there's not likely to be much danger from white damp.

"Stink damp is rare but can sometimes be dangerous. Generally, a fellow is warned away, because of the smell—which is just like rotten eggs. The worst part of stink damp is that it smells the worst when there's only a little of it. When there's so much of it around as to be deadly, it doesn't smell any worse. You get small quantities of it, sometimes, in blasting, but generally hydrogen sulphide or stink damp is found after a mine fire or an explosion. Rescue parties generally carry a cage of mice as well as one of canaries."

"With the same idea?" queried Anton.

"Exactly. As little as a tenth of one per cent. of stink damp makes a mouse sprawl on his belly, his legs don't seem strong enough to hold him up; while, in the same air, a canary doesn't suffer a bit.

"The only real danger in stink damp is when there's water in the mine, for example when, after a fire, a lot of water has been pumped down into the workings to put the fire out. Water absorbs stink damp very easily and gives it up equally easily when stirred. So, if a member of a rescue party puts his foot in a puddle of water where there has been stink damp around, so much of the gas may suddenly come up in his face as to topple him over.

"But you can see, Anton, that most of the gas troubles in a mine come from the blasting. That's why, nowadays, the miners who get out the coal seldom or never fire the shots. Experienced men, trained especially for that work, are used. After a miner has undercut the coal, the shot-firer comes. He tests for gas before he begins work, bores a deep hole in the coal with a drill, tests for gas again in case he should have tapped a leak in the seam, cleans out the hole, sends the miner for the box of explosive—which is kept thirty or forty yards away from the face where the coal is being cut—and prepares the charge with a detonater which he carries in a box over his shoulder. The miner never touches either the explosive or the detonater. Then the shot-firer puts the primed charge in the hole, jams the hole full of clay with a wooden tamper—a steel bar might cause a spark and a premature explosion—tests for gas again, connects the electric wires from a portable battery around the rib corner, fires the shot, returns to the face and tests for gas again. Then, and not until then, does the miner begin to dig the coal. That way, every one in the mine is safe."

"Yes," growled the old miner, "and the shot-firer doesn't dig any coal, nor do any hard work, an' gets paid more'n we do."

"He knows more than you do," Clem responded, "and he gets better pay because his experience and prudence is worth a lot of money to the mine. Just think what an explosion costs—to say nothing of the risk of lives being lost! And you won't find experienced shot-firers or mine-managers talking about gas sprites, Otto!"

"Better for 'em if they did!" the old man warned. "For I'm sayin' to you again, what I said before—the spirits o' the mine is gettin' hungry for blood!"

CHAPTER II
ENTOMBED ALIVE

"Danger! You're plumb crazy about danger, Clem!" Anton declared impatiently.

The older lad gestured to the big building of the pit-mouth before them, above which the spider-like legs of the headgear soared high, surmounted by the huge double winding-wheels which give so characteristic a note to a modern colliery.

"Any one who forgets that a coal-mine is dangerous is a fool," he retorted sharply, "and keep that in your head, Anton, my lad. Not that danger would ever stop me from mining. I like it. I like to feel that I'm running a risk every time I go into an entry and every time there's a blast. And I like to feel that I know enough about safety methods to snap my fingers at the risk. There's excitement in that."

"There'll be excitement enough, if old Otto's warnings come true," returned Anton gloomily.

Two days had passed since the old miner's prophecy, two days without any unusual incident. Clem had all but forgotten the evil presage, but Anton was brooding over it. It was his work to load cars in the room where Clem was mining, and the boy's superstitious nature made him painfully aware that if any accident happened to his comrade, he would probably be caught, too.

Anton had been working in the mine only a few weeks and he had not yet been able to grasp the need of Clem's incessant teaching with regard to the extreme prudence needed in colliery work. He had almost caused a serious accident during his first week by not blocking his car properly. The half-loaded car had begun to move down the slope of the mine gallery, it might easily have run clear down into the entry and possibly killed some one if Clem had not dashed forward and checked the car before it had too much speed.

In general, Anton had not reasoned much about the danger or the lack of danger in coal-mining. He regarded the pit as a matter of course. It was the only life he knew. All his comrades were at work in the mine or would be at work therein, as soon as their school-days were over. The boy himself had started early, soon after his father's death, since it was the only employment to be got in the neighborhood and he had his widowed mother to support.

Clem had found a place in the mine for his friend without any difficulty, for Anton was powerfully muscled. In this he took after his father, who had been almost a Hercules and one of the champion wrestlers of the mine. Born of miner stock on both sides, Anton was short and squat, able to shovel coal all day without fatigue. He had accordingly, been taken on as a loader, Clem undertaking to keep an eye over him.

It took the older lad all his time to do so. Anton was absolutely reckless by nature, and, though he was constantly being advised as to the necessary precautions for making mining safe, he could never be persuaded to adopt them.

Instead of blocking his car with one log placed across the track and another under the car and resting on the transverse log, he would put a piece of coal under the wheel and trust to its staying there; he would wear his coat loosely, over his trousers, though he was told over and over again that he ran the risk of his coat being caught by the cars, when switching, and being dragged along the side of the rib: on another occasion, Clem found the boy starting along the haulage-way used for the coal cars instead of using the man-way reserved for the workers, in order to save a couple of minutes' time.

What exasperated Clem even more was that, since Otto's warning, Anton had become more careless than ever. It was evident that the fatalistic streak in the boy made him feel that if he were foredoomed to an accident, there was no use in trying to prevent it.

The boy's impatient exclamation and his comrade's retort about danger had occurred while they were in line in front of the lamp shack, waiting to get their safety-lamps before going down for the day shift.

As in most well-organized collieries, the safety-lamps were filled and adjusted by experts, who looked after nothing else. After the lamps were lighted, they were locked — and not one of the miners was allowed a key. Thus the lamps could not be opened below ground and there was no chance for a reckless man to expose a naked flame in a room or entry where there might chance to be gas. A safety-lamp would not go out unless the air in the mine was so vitiated that it was dangerous to life to remain therein, or unless there was some defect in the lamp which would render it perilous to use.

After the lamps had been given out, Clem and Anton got in the cage to go down the shaft. Otto happened to be descending at the same time.

"We're still waiting for your 'knockers' to show themselves!" Clem suggested jestingly.

The old man deigned no reply. Instead, he looked round the cage meaningly at the other men there, most of whom frowned at Clem's remark. Among miners, it is believed to bring bad luck to speak or even to hint of accidents when in the cage. Only Otto's personal liking for the young fellow kept him from a retort which might have brought on a quarrel.

On reaching the bottom, Clem and Anton set out along the man-way together. It was a walk of nearly a mile underground from the main shaft of the mine to the distant "room" or square hole in the seam, where Clem was to dig away the coal face, and which was one of the rooms from which Anton was loading coal.

This Ohio colliery was being worked on what is known as the pillar-and-room method. This consists in dividing the seam of coal into squares like a chessboard, taking out the coal from each alternate square, leaving the intervening squares of coal intact to act as pillars in holding up the roof. They do not look like pillars to a careless observer, often being blocks of coal thirty yards square.

"It seems silly," said Anton, after they had walked on a minute or two, "to leave all this coal near the shaft and to go digging a mile away. Why not take all the coal that is handy first?"

"And have the roof come down and block up all the coal that is beyond? That would be just throwing away the wealth of the mine."

"Timber the roof, then!"

"It would cost too much, for one thing," Clem explained, "and, for another, all the timber in the world won't hold up a roof if the excavation is made too big. There's millions of tons of rock pressing down on a mine roof. Judging by the way you talk, Anton, I don't believe you understand what a coal formation is, yet."

"Isn't it like Otto said, then?"

"Only in a way. Otto's description of the coal forests was near enough — in spite of his ideas about goblins and sprites — and he was correct in saying that the forests decayed under water and turned into coal after they were pressed down by rock. But it wasn't the Flood that did that, at least not the Flood that Otto was speaking of. The coal forests existed millions of years before Noah.

"What's more, it wasn't only just once that the forests were covered by a deluge. That happened several times, a hundred or more, in some places.

"For centuries at a time, these gloomy and steaming forests grew in boggy land, only a few inches above the level of the sea. Gradually the land sank, the sea came in, the trees fell and decayed under the water, and a layer of mud or sand was deposited over them. Then gradually the land rose again just above the level of the sea, and a new forest grew. Once more the land sank below the water, the second forest fell into decay and upon that layer a new deposit of mud or sand was laid. That gave two layers or seams of coal-forest-bog, to be turned later into coal by pressure; and two layers or strata of mud or sand, to be turned into shale and slate or into sandstone, also by pressure.

"When a long time elapsed between the swampings, several centuries of coal forests had made a deep bed of bog, which, ages after, became a thickseam of coal. When the swampings happened close together, the layer of bog was shallow, producing a thin seam of coal. In the same way, the layers of shale or sandstone are thick or thin according to the length of time that the land was under the water.

"Because of that, Anton, in nearly every colliery there is not just one layer or seam of coal, but a number of them. There are sixteen different seams in this mine, showing that the land rose and fell sixteen times, probably in the course of a million years.

"Some mines show much bigger changes. In the famous coal basin of Mons, in Belgium, there are 157 layers of coal, of which 120 are thick enough to be workable. The Saar basin, on the left bank of the Rhine, which has played so important a part in the international troubles following the end of the World War, has 164 seams, with 77 of them workable, giving a thickness of 240 feet of coal. However, as the lowest layers are nearly four miles deep, they will probably never be worked."

"Why not?"

"To start with, the cost of haulage to the top would be enormous. But, aside from that, a good many mining engineers figure that the temperature at that depth would be above boiling point. You know, in general, the farther you go down in a mine, the hotter it gets."

"What do you mean by a seam being 'workable'?" the boy queried. "Can't all coal be dug out?"

"Not by a long shot. At least not so as to be worked at a profit. Suppose a seam of coal is only a few inches thick, how is a miner going to dig it out? He couldn't crawl in such a seam, let alone using his tools there."

"He could cut out enough rock at the top and bottom to give him a chance to get in."

"A miner is paid for digging coal, not digging rock," was the answer. "What's more, according to your scheme, so much shale or sandstone would be mixed with the coal that it would be useless for burning.

"Even seams two feet thick are so hard to work that most of them are left alone, and a seam three feet thick means extra expense in getting out the coal because of the difficulty of labor in hewing and transporting the coal from the face to the shaft. The ideal thickness is between six and eight feet, where a man can stand upright and can reach to the roof with a slate bar. That height, too, makes timbering easy.

"Very thick seams have their own difficulties. The worst of these is the supporting of the roof. Take a seam 30 or 40 feet thick, for example. Look at the size of the hole that is left when the coal is dug away! Timbering becomes a real problem, there, for the longer a prop is, Anton, the weaker it is. Coal managers in mines like those have to do some careful figuring, or the cost of the timber they put into the mine would be more than the value of the coal they take out."

"How do they handle it then?"

"As if it were a quarry, rather than a mine. The seam is worked on successive levels, but, even then, it is impossible to prevent constant accidents from the fall of coal or the sudden collapse of a roof. Take it the world over, and ten miners are killed every day in collieries alone. I told you coal mining was dangerous."

"But are there any of those thick seams in the United States?"

"None of the really thick ones. There's a 40-foot anthracite seam in Pennsylvania. But in France, near the famous Creusot works, there's a bed of coal which is 130 feet thick. It's a basin, though, rather than a seam.

"So you see, Anton, every coal mine is different, with its layers or seams of coal of different thicknesses and at varying distances apart. Some pits are near the surface, some are very deep; some coal is full of gas, other has very little; some coal is so hard that every bit of it has to be blasted, in other mines the coal is so soft that the hewer spends half his time spragging the face so that the coal doesn't fall on him when he's undercutting or holing. Don't you make the mistake of thinking that all a miner has to do is to use his pick! He's got to know his business thoroughly or he's useless to the mine boss and a danger to all his fellow-workmen.

"And that isn't all, Anton, not by a good deal!

"Coal mining might be bad enough, even if the coal seams always ran level. But it's very seldom that they do. They run up-hill and down-hill in all sorts of fashions and play hide-and-go-seek in a way that's fairly bewildering.

"Nearly all coal seams are broken up by faults. The coal suddenly seems to stop, and, when you go to hewing it the pick suddenly hits against a rock wall, right on the level of the seam. In the North Gallery of this very mine, there's a fault like that. You know where the 'snagger' is?"

"Sure," agreed Anton, "you mean where the cars have to be hitched on to a chain?"

"Yes, there! The coal seam jumps upwards fifty feet. That's why the cars, after rolling down nearly a quarter of a mile, by gravity, have to be pulled up fifty feet by an endless chain, to rejoin the same seam and then to go rolling on down by themselves."

"Just what are faults?"

"H'm, that's a bit hard to explain to you, Anton, because you don't know anything about geology, but maybe I can get you to see. Faults are breaks in the layers of rock, or in the stratification, as it is called. All coal seams and the rocks above and below them have been laid down by water. Since water levels everything, these layers of rock were level, once.

"In ages past, however, the crust of the earth changed a good deal. As the crust cooled, it contracted, crumpling up these different layers into all sorts of shapes. Sometimes it bulged them up, sometimes it hollowed them down so that the edges rose. Quite often a layer of rock would be cracked right across, and one half would stay level while the other shot up almost a right angle. A good many mountains show the result of this, and if you look at such rocks as are sticking up out of the ground you will see some of them standing right on edge. Once in a while, part of the broken crust slid over the other part. Then, too, though the surface may not always show it, there have been breaks in the strata below, and at the break, the layer has sunk or risen quite a distance from its former level.

23

"If that happens to a coal seam, you can see that where the seam breaks, suddenly, the rest of it will continue on another level, perhaps only a few feet higher or lower, perhaps a good deal more. It's up to the mine geologist to find where the coal has gone to, and it's the business of the mine engineer to remodel the entire system of working the mine in order to get at that seam."

"And are all coal mines mixed up in that funny way?" Anton queried.

"Most of them. Oh, there's no end to the tricks a coal seam can play. A deep coal seam may split into two narrow ones, too thin to work. The whole seam may quickly dwindle away to nothing, showing that, in ages past, a river came rolling over it and washed away all the forest bog. Sometimes, especially with the lowermost seams, the forest grew on rolling land, so that the bottom of the coal seam is irregular, causing all sorts of trouble in laying rails for the cars to roll on. Sometimes the layer of rock under a coal seam is so soft that when you start to timber it, the timbers sink into the floor and the roof comes toppling down.

"Among the queerest of all the things a mine geologist strikes are what are called dykes. These are great shafts of igneous rock, which were thrust up from the interior of the earth in a white-hot state and which burned away the coal as they rose. They put a dead stop to a working. I could tell you a dozen more freak things that a coal seam can do. A mine geologist has not only a new problem to tackle with every mine, but, often, with every mine gallery."

"Is that what you're studying to be, Clem?"

"No, indeed!" The young fellow's answer was emphatic. "That's 'way out of my reach. It takes a college man, with special technical training and a big experience, to be anything of a mine geologist. All I'm trying to do is to learn enough about it so that when I get to be a mine boss — if I ever do — I'll know what my chiefs are trying to do and I'll be able to help them.

"Take Otto, for example. There isn't a better worker in the mine. He gets out more coal and less broken stuff than any other man below ground. But he'll never be anything but a hewer, because he doesn't want to learn. Why, just the other day, he was growling because the mine was shut down to repair one of the shafts, though the other shaft was working all right."

"So were a lot of the men," Anton put in. "Why couldn't they go on working, with one shaft?"

"Against the law," was the crisp answer. "That's the A B C of mining. And I'll show you why! All mines are required to have two shafts, in case of accident. That law was passed because of a famous disaster that happened in England nearly a hundred years ago.

"In those days, colliers had only one shaft. One day, the beam of an engine which was directly over a shaft snapped, and a huge piece of machinery, weighing several tons, tumbled into the shaft and stuck, not far from the bottom. As it fell, it ripped away the planking which lined the shaft and a whole lot of loose rock and earth fell on top of the piece of machinery, blocking up the shaft entirely and stopping any air from passing. There were over two hundred men and boys at work below ground.

"With only one shaft, you can see what a mess that made! Before any digging could be done, the lining of the shaft had to be repaired, because dirt and rocks were falling into the shaft all the time. Miners—hundreds of them—were brought from neighboring mines, and they worked night and day on two-hour shifts, clinging to the sides of the shaft as thick as bees in a hive. Others, risking their lives with every stroke of the pick, dug away at the earth and rock that had fallen on the big chunk of machinery. With all the speed that human effort could compass, it was six days and nights before a hole had been made through the obstruction big enough for a man to pass. And, when the first rescuer reached the workings below, the 200 men were dead. Not a single one survived. The miners had been entombed alive without any air passage and could do nothing, absolutely nothing, to help themselves out of their living grave.

"Ever since then, every colliery in Europe and the United States is required to have two shafts, and the law demands that these shall be no less than fifteen yards apart and connected by a wide passage. Not only that, but each shaft must have a complete outfit of winding machinery coupled to separate engines, so that, in the event of an accident happening to one shaft, the men below ground can be rescued up the other."

"That sounds all right," said Anton, rather gloomily, "but suppose the way to both shafts is blocked?"

"Not likely," Clem responded cheerfully, "if a mine has been properly laid out. Take this one, there are half a dozen ways to get from the face to the shaft."

"But Otto said —"

The other turned upon him sharply.

"I've had about enough of that Otto business! If you can't keep from thinking about it, keep from talking about it, anyhow!"

To this rebuke Anton maintained a stubborn silence, and, without another word said, the two walked on until they reached their respective places of work.

In the gloomy world of below ground, where the dusty wall of sooty black is the only landscape to be seen, one day is very much like another. Reaching his room, Clem stood his tools in order along the rib, hung his safety lamp on a nail which he drove into a prop supporting the roof, and, reaching up so as to put one hand on the roof, tapped it with the flat side of his pick to make sure that there was no loose slate overhead. He then examined the coal face, as it had been left by the hewer who had been working on the night shift, to make sure that it had been properly spragged or timbered.

This done, Clem stripped naked to the waist, for it was hot in that hole far below ground. Then, lying down flat on his side, his bare shoulder resting on the gritty ground, he started to pick away the coal at the level of the floor and just above it, making a wedge-shaped hole extending under the seam for a distance in of three feet.

Many mines, especially in America, use mechanical coal-cutters for this back-breaking labor. These machines are especially useful in mines where the coal-seams are less than 3-1/2 feet thick, and they are well adapted to "long-wall" workings where the whole face of the coal is removed in a single operation. Some are mounted with a toothed bar which moves in and out, chipping the coal; other types are like circular saws; several forms have the same action as a miner's pick, the percussions being at the speed of two hundred strokes a minute, the motive-power being compressed air.

In pillar-and-room workings, such as this Ohio mine, chain heading machines were used. This American invention consists of a bed-plate which rests on the floor and is secured in position by screw-jacks braced against the roof and against the rib. On this bed-plate rests a sliding frame which carries a revolving chain on which cutting tools are fixed. The machine carries its own motor, which not only drives the chain, but also slides forward the frame into the cut. When the cut is made to the full depth of the machine, it is withdrawn, and the machine moved over its own width and another cut commenced. Several of these machines were at work in the mine, but chiefly in that part of it where the pillars were being cut away, and where speed in removing the coal was a prime necessity. In the more distant rooms, hand labor was used.

All these machines work on exactly the same principle as that of the miner, lying on his back or on his side, and digging at the coal with his pick. The coal must be undercut as far in as a pick or a mechanical coal-cutter will reach, for the entire width of the face. Every few feet, short props or sprags are put in from the edge of the undermined portion to the floor, to prevent a premature fall, which might bury the miner.

When the whole face is undercut and spragged, the shot-firer is summoned. One or more holes, three feet deep, are bored in the coal, close to the roof, these holes are filled with explosive and tamped shut with moist clay, and the charges are fired. This blasting brings down the coal off the face, clear from the rock roof to the undermined portion, for such a distance as it has been undercut.

The miner then shovels away the coal far enough to allow him to lie down again and continue his terribly laborious task, while the loader comes and shovels the blasted coal into cars or into endless-chain conveyors, according to the arrangement of the mine.

27

Day in, day out, this hewing continues. While the miner is at work, he is always in a cramped position, his body twisted, his muscles at a strain, performing his toilsome labor in the half-dark, in the heat, in poor air, choked with coal-dust constantly and menaced by death every moment. He is well paid, but most fully does he earn every cent he gets.

The morning had almost passed, and Anton was near the entry, where he heard, in the distance, a dull rumble like thunder, followed by a queer cracking sound which seemed to travel along the rock overhead.

The boy halted involuntarily in his task of pushing an empty car back to a room for loading. Little as he knew of the noises below ground, he sensed something strange. The deep silence of a coal mine is generally broken only by the sharp report of a blast or the rattle of cars, and this rumble did not resemble either sound.

A second or two later, a miner dashed past him, without his tools, his safety-lamp swinging as he ran.

"The bank is coming down!" he yelled, and disappeared down the gallery.

Almost at the same moment, another man came out of the entry, his naked back gleaming as he passed under the electric light hanging at the opening of the entry.

"Make for the shaft, kid!" he shouted, when he saw the shine of Anton's lamp.

A sudden babble of excited cries, borne on the strong current of the ventilating air, reached the boy's ears.

It was the doom of Otto's warning!

Shoving a lump of coal under the car-wheel, Anton whirled on his heel to follow the escaping miners, when, like a blow, came the stunning thought:

"Clem!"

He hesitated an instant, and, while he halted, a second and a louder crash told him that the fall of rock—wherever it might be happening—was not over. Every fraction of a second that he delayed might ruin his chances of escape.

But Anton was of sturdy miner stock, and, in addition, was thoroughly fatalistic. That very feature of his character which his older comrade had blamed so often, now was to show its good side. If he were going to be caught by the fall, there was no use in his trying to prevent it, he thought.

In any case, no matter what might come, though the roof cracked above him and the coal-ribs crushed beside him, he must warn his friend.

Turning his back to the way of hope, he tore at his utmost speed towards the room where Clem was working, taking some small comfort, as he ran, that the rumbling sounded farther and farther away.

"Clem!" he cried, panting, as he turned into the room where his friend was digging coal, "run for your life!"

By the terror in Anton's voice, the young fellow realized the peril. In his isolated room, he had not heard a sound.

Leaping to his feet and grabbing his safety-lamp from the prop, he ran after Anton, who had started back on the road leading to the shaft. Fleeter of foot than the boy, he caught up with him in a few yards.

"What is it?" he queried.

"The bank's down!"

"Where?"

"I don't know. Everywhere. The whole mine's smashing! Every one else has got out long ago!"

An ominous creaking sounded over their heads.

Clem caught his comrade by the arm and pulled him into a narrow entry near by.

"Go slow! We don't want to get smashed!"

He held up his safety-lamp.

"Look at that prop!"

The heavy timber was bending like a twig.

"Get on quick!" cried Anton, struggling against the grasp, but the young fellow held him fast.

"Don't lose your head!" he warned. "The current of air has stopped, sure sign that the way to the shafts is blocked. The nearer we get to the goaf (waste ground), the more likely we are to get crushed. Listen!"

The creaking grew louder, and then, suddenly, with a rush of sound, the gallery in front of them, into which Anton had been about to plunge, sagged. The bending prop went into splinters, and, with a roar, the whole roof fell, the broken rock coming to within a few yards of where they were standing.

"Close shave, that!" remarked Clem coolly.

Anton made no answer, but shivered as he looked. He realized that his comrade's warning had saved his life.

The trembling and the creaking recommenced, but farther away; then, with a gigantic noise of tearing, there came a rending crash, followed by utter silence.

"Now!"

He let go the boy's arm and turned sharp off to the right.

"That's not the way to the shaft," protested Anton.

"We'll try the North Gallery," answered Clem. "Likely enough the fall has followed the line of the fault."

A sharp run of a hundred yards brought them to a pile of rock blocking up the passage. Clem licked his hand to make it moist, and then slowly passed it across the entire face of the obstruction.

"No!" he said. "There's not a breath of air coming through. That way's blocked."

He turned in another direction. With all the ventilation stopped, the air was growing heavy. Fifty yards' run, and then—

Blocked again!

This time Clem made no comment. He turned back to try the farther side of the mine. As they wheeled round a corner, and saw a gleam of light he cried, with a note of relief:

"There they are! I knew they'd send in a rescue party, right away!"

Then his voice dropped.

"No," he added, "there's only one lamp."

A single miner came running towards them.

"The North Gallery?" he queried.

"No good, Jim," Clem answered, who recognized him as a new-comer in the mine. "Blocked solid!"

"So's the entries to the goaf! I've been there! How about the old workings I've heard the boys talk of?"

The student miner shook his head.

"Not much chance that way, I'm afraid. They'll be full of gas, sure. The ventilation has been cut out of there for months. But we can try it, anyway."

"I'd ought to ha' known better'n to work this shift," declared Jim, as they ran. "You mind when you talked to Otto in the cage, comin' down?"

"Yes."

"Well, Otto wouldn't go to work, nohow. Said the knockers had been riled an' he wouldn't take the risk o' goin' agin 'em. The boss swore at him some, but that didn' faze Otto. He went to the top, just the same. He had the right hunch. Wish I'd followed him!"

They ran on, and Jim broke out again:

"I'd no business to come coal minin', anyway. I'm a prospector, by rights. Gold's my end, not coal. You're s'posed to know this game. What chance ha' we got?"

Clem made no answer in words. He held up his safety-lamp, already showing a marked blue cap of gas over the flame.

"I'd seen it a'ready! That means gas, don't it?"

"We may get through it," said Clem, but his tone was not hopeful.

They turned into a long gallery leading to the old workings, and, as they sped along, the cones of gas on the safety lamps grew longer and longer.

Presently lumps of slate and rock on the floor heralded the end.

Quite suddenly, the gleam of the lamps shone on a wall before them. The roof had fallen in.

"That's the last chance?" queried Anton, gloomily.

"The very last," said Clem, "we're buried."

CHAPTER III
THE DANGERS OF RESCUE

The midday whistle of the mine had just begun, when a violent blast of air roared up the intake shaft, followed by a portentous —

Cra-a-ack!

A terrific crash rose from the bowels of the earth.

The growling rumble of the underground disaster came rolling upward in throbbing volumes of sound.

The ground trembled, the buildings shook, the lofty skeleton of the pit-head gear wavered as though about to let fall the huge revolving wheels overhead.

From the engine-house, from the pumping-room, from the ventilation building, from the screeners and washers, from the picking-belts, from the loading-yards, from the coking-ovens, from every corner of the vast above-ground works of a modern colliery, the men came running.

Some were white of face, some sooty, but all bore an expression of the most extreme anxiety.

The mine superintendent, who was also the owner, the mine boss, and the mining engineer were among the first at the shaft. The doctor and hospital attendant — whom the law requires to be maintained at all mines employing more than a hundred men — arrived but a few seconds later.

The superintendent, a vigorous Australian, who had taken part in many a sensational mining rush in his youth, and who had inherited the ownership of this coal mine from a distant relative but a few years before, leaped into action. Orders came rattling like hail.

All haulage of coal from below was stopped. The engine on the second shaft was thrown into gear, and the cages in both shafts were sent down to bring up the men.

Would there be any to bring?

What did the crash denote? A mere fall of roof, which might cause the loss of a few lives, or a vast explosion which would sweep every man below ground to death in a few seconds?

The cages had hardly reached the bottom when there came the second crash.

The crowd around the shaft was thickening. The doors of the hundreds of cottages clustered in rows about the colliery had been thrown open; from every direction the women came running, their shawls streaming behind them. Many of them had already lost fathers or husbands or sons below ground; all knew the awful menace of that sickening rumble.

With all the speed that the winding-engines could be made to give, the cages were hauled up. They had not yet reached the top when a sudden cry of horror arose. Otto, who had not gone home, despite his abandonment of the day's work, but who had hung around the pit-head all day, pointed with his finger to the steep hillside that rose abruptly above the mine.

The hill itself was falling!

The pine forest swayed, as though the huge trees were but blades of grass, seemed to move downward a few yards, sending up a cloud of dust, and then fairly plunged down the slope in an avalanche of rocks, trees and earth mixed with tremendous bowlders. With a roar like the fall of a near-by thunderbolt, the landslide ripped away the side of the hill, the ground settling with a shiver like that of an earthquake, and sagging perceptibly.

"Sound the emergency whistle!" came the command.

A minute or two later, a series of shrill screeches gave the signal for summoning the rescue corps. Nearly all American mines, following the requirements and suggestions of the U. S. Bureau of Mines, maintain elaborately equipped rescue stations, manned by picked miners who are regularly drilled in the use of the apparatus.

Before the emergency signal had finished sounding the second time, both the rescue team and the first-aid team were at their places. Simultaneously, the cages containing the first load of miners came to the top.

A great sigh of relief went up.

"Well?" queried the superintendent to one of the mine foremen, who was in the first cage.

"A big roof-fall, sir," was the reply. "It was still fallin' when I came up. I left Lloyd to handle the men at the bottom while I came up to report."

"Gas?"

"None showin' as yet, sir. But I came right away. It might gather a bit later."

"How many missing?"

"Can't tell, sir. Most o' the men seemed to be gettin' clear."

"Ready to go down again?"

"Sure!"

"All right, get in the cage, then."

The assistant superintendent, the mining engineer, the safety inspector, and the fire boss were already in. The foreman jumped in beside them, and the cage rattled down to the bottom.

Already the word had spread to the gathering crowd that the accident was but a roof-fall, not an explosion, that two cages full of miners had come and that there was a likelihood that most of the men were safe.

Volunteers clustered around the mine-owner, clamoring to be allowed to go down.

"We'll dig 'em out, sir!" they cried cheerily.

"Keep back, men!" was the answer. "Wait till we know just what has to be done. Maybe every one below ground will have a chance to get out."

There was need for caution. While mine disasters are numerous — over two thousand men being killed every year in United States collieries alone — such an accident as this one had rarely happened before. The landslide above, combined with the sinking of the strata below, produced a condition which might be of the extremest danger.

The foreman of the pumping plant was the first to find evidence of this trouble. He hurried forward, consternation on his face.

"Mr Owens, the pumps have quit working!"

"What's wrong?"

"Pipes busted, sir, probably. The turbine's goin' all right, but she's suckin' air."

"How much water were you throwing this morning?"

"Over three thousand gallons an hour, sir."

"H'm, it won't take long to drown the mine at that rate. And if there are any poor fellows cut off—"

He turned to the store-house keeper.

"Got plenty of spare pipe?"

"Lots of it, sir."

"Get it out!"

Then, to the mine boss:

"Murchison, get a new pipe down the uptake shaft as quick as you know how! Double pay for every man working on the job! Put them on the jump!"

As fast as his eye could travel round the circle of eager men, the boss picked his workers, miners of tried worth.

Almost as though by magic a line was formed from the storehouse to the shaft. Mechanics, with their tools ready, were on the ladders by the time the first joint of pipe reached the shaft, and the first nine-foot length was flanged on in less than five minutes after the giving of the order. So fast were the joints thimbled and braced against the side of the shaft that the long pipe seemed to grow like a living thing. In an hour's time, the pumps were going again.

Meanwhile, the time clerk, not needing to wait for his orders, had checked the names of all the men who had come up the shaft, until the cage came up empty save for the foreman.

"That's the last," he said.

The time clerk closed his book and nodded, then went to the superintendent.

"Eight missing, sir."

"That's bad enough, though it might have been a good deal worse. Make out a detailed list and bring it here."

Truly it was bad enough. The fire boss and safety engineer had reported that fire had broken out in some part of the mine, probably, for white damp was leaking through. The report of the mining engineer was graver still. The first subsidence of the mine had caused the landslide, and the shock of the landslide had crushed all the galleries leading from the shafts.

"You mean that all the workings are smashed in?"

"I wouldn't say that. They can't be, the way the workings are laid out. But there's more rock to be cleared away than I like to think about. How many men are caught?"

"Eight."

"Do you know whereabouts, Mr Owens?"

"I'll tell you in a minute. Here's the clerk now." He scanned the list. "Well, three of them were working in the end galleries."

"They might be safe," interjected the mining engineer. "That's under the hill."

"Two of them," the superintendent continued, "were working in the broken, out towards the old workings, and the other three were near the North Gallery."

"We might get at the last three, but, judging from the lie, the old workings section will be choked until Doomsday."

"You mean we can't try to get those two men out?"

The mining engineer looked his chief full in the face.

"No, you can't," he said bluntly. "There's a fair chance of rescue in the North Gallery section, and, as for the others, we might drive galleries through to the rooms under the hill—though it'll take some time. The two men in the old workings are gone. They're probably smashed under the fall, anyway."

"I'll get all those men out or break my neck trying!" burst out the owner of the mine.

"If you scatter your forces, you won't do anything," the mining engineer retorted. As an expert in his profession, he was prepared to back his own opinion against all the officials of the mine, from the owner down, the more so as he knew that his chief had not spent his life in coal mining.

Owens glared at him, but he knew that the engineer was right.

"Lay out the work, then, since you know so much! I'll have the gangs ready, by the time you are. You think the men in the end galleries can be got at?"

"I'm sure of it, if they hold out long enough, and if they're lucky enough to escape the damps. Our main trouble is going to be the timbering. Now, the farther in we go, the farther we get from the break. The roof will be solid back there, most likely. That's why I think a good chance of rescue lies that way."

"Get at that end first, then. Clem Swinton's in that group of men. I'd be sorry to lose him. He's the most promising young fellow in the mine."

The mining engineer nodded.

"I know him. He's been attending the night school. You're right. We can't afford to lose him. It's easy enough to find miners—especially foreigners—but a young American who wants to learn the colliery business thoroughly is rare. I've had my eye on him, too."

At this point, Otto, who had been edging near his superiors and who had overheard the conversation, broke in.

"You don't need to worry over Clem Swinton, Mr. Owens," he said. "Clem'll get a good scare out o' this, an' that's about all."

"How do you know, Otto?" The superintendent spoke good-humoredly, for he knew and liked the old man. On more than one occasion, when astrike was threatened Otto's good sense had held back his fellow-miners from violent measures, and his chiefs recognized both his popularity and his loyalty. "Did your friends the 'knockers' tell you so?"

"They did, Mr Owens," was the unperturbed answer. "You'll see if I ain't right!"

"I hope you are. I'll put you in charge of one of the gangs at that end, if you like."

"I was a-goin' to," responded Otto, who had never doubted that he would be chosen for the post.

By four o'clock in the afternoon, work had been thoroughly organized. The pumps had got control of the water, a temporary ventilating circuit had been established in an effort to keep the mine air pure—for the main system had been destroyed by the fall, and the mining gangs were at work, digging away the obstruction and loading with feverish haste.

This was a very different matter from hewing coal, which is always laid out in regular seams and naturally divided by splitting planes. The rock from the strata above had fallen into the galleries at all angles, and was mixed up with the crushed and partly splintered timbers of the roof and sides. Blasting had to be done on a small scale and with extreme caution, for there was fire damp in the mine, due to the lack of complete ventilation.

The road-bed and rails, on which the cars for the transporting of the débris must run, were flattened and twisted. It was necessary to lay down new rails, however shakily. Moreover, since all the coal conveyors and electric haulage systems were a tangle of wreckage, the loaded cars had to be pushed by hand all the way along the underground galleries, to the bottom of the shaft.

The timbering gangs had a desperate job to do, for there was no solid flat roof overhead under which props could be put, nor could enough time be given to build a stable timber roof. Yet, upon the ability of the timber boss hung the lives of all the rescuers.

Night came, but without any slacking of the work. The electrical engineer and his staff strung temporary wires, and, both below ground and above ground, the colliery workings were as bright as day.

The scene was one of furious rush. Neighboring mines sent gangs to help. Cars loaded with mine timbers came from all the near-by collieries. The news of the accident, published in the local evening papers, had brought offers of help from every quarter. Before midnight, officials from the Bureau of Mines were on the scene.

At 3 o'clock in the morning, one of the great Rescue Cars maintained by the Bureau rolled into the railroad yards of the colliery. In this car were experts whose principal work was the direction of rescue operations in mining disasters, and the car contained a complete equipment of all the most modern scientific appliances.

The first rays of Saturday's dawn showed the crowd still gathered around the shaft. Owens, hollow-eyed from lack of sleep and from watching, was still directing the operations, but with the advice and assistance of government officials.

The work was proceeding apace. The miners' picks rang incessantly, without a second's pause, each man streaming with perspiration as he toiled. Rails were put down as fast as the obstruction was dug away. The timber gangs strove like madmen. Each shift was for two hours only, with no pause between, for there were men and to spare.

So the day and the night passed.

At ten o'clock on Sunday morning, there came a cry —

"She's fallin' again!"

A tremor ran through the mine.

Another shifting of the strata imperilled all the excavation that had been done.

A few minutes' hesitation might have been fatal, but the timber gangs rushed forward, though the props were bending on every side of them and threatened, from second to second, to engulf them in falling rock. In a haste that approached to panic, timbers were thrust up and braced, so that but a small section of the roof fell.

Some of the miners quit, the more readily as a couple of them were badly hurt in the little fall, but for every man who showed the white feather, there were a score to volunteer. They were led by Owens himself, who was at the bottom of the shaft when the fall came. With all the fire of his adventurous youth, he seized a pick and ran forward to the most dangerous place, crying:

"Those men are to be got out, or I'll die down here with them! Who follows?"

There was no farther talk of quitting.

On Monday there arrived from Washington a Bureau of Mines expert, with a new listening-device, known as a geophone. This is an instrument worked on the microphone plan, so sensitive that it responds to the slightest vibration, even through dense rock-strata, hundreds of feet thick.

"Stop work, all!" came the order. "Not a word, not a whisper! Keep your feet and hands as still as if you were frozen!"

There was a tense five minutes as the geophone expert listened.

Presently he detached from his head the ear-clamps leading to the microphone receiver.

"The men are alive!" he declared. "I hear them knocking!"

"To work, men!" cried the boss, and the picks rang with redoubled zest.

It was Tuesday, shortly before dawn, when the rescuers pierced the first obstruction, only to find another and a worse break beyond.

A draft of air sucked through. Almost immediately the caps of the safety lamps showed blue. At the same time, the safety inspector called, "Back from the face, men! Back, all!"

He pointed to the little cage he had been holding.

The canaries had collapsed!

Carbon monoxide was pouring out, the deadly white damp, that kills as it strikes!

The hewers retreated, grumbling.

"We can stand it, with reliefs!" they declared.

But the Bureau man was adamant.

"Get back when you're told," he said shortly. "We'll get those men out all right. Bring the gas gang here!"

Then it was that the researches of the trained workers of the Bureau of Mines showed to their best advantage.

Along the gallery came a line of strange-eyed and humped figures, inhuman of appearance, wearing the newly devised respirators by which men can work in the most vitiated air without harm.

There are several types of these "gas masks," most of them based on the principle of carrying compressed oxygen for breathing, and bearing chambers containing chemicals which absorb the carbonic acid gas and moisture of the exhaled breath. These masks proved their utility at the great explosion at Courrières in 1906, the greatest mining disaster on record, when 1100 miners were killed.

It was not long, however, before it became evident that there was a limit to the usefulness of the respirators. Excellent as they were for exploring galleries filled with poisonous gas, it was difficult to do fast digging in them. The work slowed down.

"Look here, Mr. Owens," protested Otto, "if we don't go no faster'n we're goin' now, it'll be a month afore we get through. Let us go in! If the gas is bad, we'll take hour shifts, or half-hour shifts, or ten-minute shifts, if it comes to that! The men'll tough it out as long as they can!"

"What about it?" said the superintendent, to the Director of the Bureau of Mines car.

"If the men are willing to take the risk! But we can purify the air to some extent, anyway. I've a man down there with a Burrell gas detector, which is several hundred times more sensitive than any canary, so that we can keep a close watch on the air changes, and there are plenty of tanks of compressed oxygen to be got. I've some here in the car, and a telegram to Pittsburgh will bring us more in a few hours. We can put in another bellows, too.

"This miner's right enough, about the digging. Fast work can't be done in respirators. The men will have to use electric cap lamps, of course, but I've a big supply in the car."

Back into the poisoned air the miners went. That strain soon tested out the men, and, as the old miner had said to Clem, a week before, the young men and the single men were compelled to give up, first. Old Otto stood up to his work with the best of them, but forty minutes at a stretch was as long as any of the men could stand.

On Tuesday night, the rescuers working out from the up-take shaft broke through the obstruction into the North Gallery. The three men who had been imprisoned there were found asleep, close to the sleep that knows no waking, terribly poisoned by the lack of oxygen.

The mine doctor, who had been waiting at the face until the moment of breaking through, was the first through the hole. Rapidly he examined the unconscious men.

"One's nearly gone," he shouted back, "but I reckon we can save all three!"

A mighty cheer rolled through the galleries at the news that the North Gallery men were saved. It was echoed at the shaft and above ground.

Without loss of time, the men were brought to the open air and rushed to the mine hospital. Two hours passed before the first of them recovered consciousness.

The geophone expert was at his bedside, waiting impatiently.

"Have you been knocking any signals lately?" he asked, eagerly, as soon as the survivor was able to speak.

"No," the miner answered feebly, "we'd gave up. Thought it wasn't no use."

"I heard knocking again this morning," the expert announced. "The men at the far galleries must be alive still!"

Wednesday saw no diminution of the endeavor, but more than half the miners of the rescue crews were down and out, suffering to a greater or lesser degree from the terrible strain of the short shifts in the deadly mixture of fire damp and white damp. Yet volunteers were as plentiful as ever, for both the mine managers and the miners of neighboring collieries stood ready to help.

By Wednesday night came the cheering news that the roof overhead was more solid and that the rock fall had not broken in the floor. The cars rattled in and out, a car to each shaft in less than three minutes, loaded and pushed by willing hands. With the North Gallery men saved, both shafts had been set hauling the débris from the galleries leading to where Clem, Anton, and Jim were imprisoned.

At breakfast time, Thursday morning, just at the change of shift, the geophone expert reported voices.

The message was sped aloft:

"The men are still alive! We have heard them talking!"

The news seemed too good to be credited. Seven days the three men had been entombed, seven days without food, water or light, seven days in foul air, probably impregnated with noxious vapors.

Suddenly, at 3 o'clock in the afternoon, the signal came from below to the pit-head to cease hauling.

What had happened?

There could be but one explanation. The cars must have stopped.

There had been another fall in the mine, blocking off the gallery.

The rescuers were caught!

Like wild-fire the news spread through the mining village.

Great and excited as had been the crowd before, it was ten times more excited now. Women, whose husbands were in the rescue gang, shook their fists at Owens, clamoring that he had sent fifty men to death in order to save three. The animosity spread to the miners who had lacked the nerve to volunteer, and all sorts of wild rumors passed among the crowd.

There might have been serious trouble, but the gates of the high fences around the pit-head enclosure had been closed, and the mine guards, armed with rifles, patrolled the place. Ever since the days of the "Molly Maguires," — and many much more recent bloody outbreaks among coal miners — colliery owners have maintained armed guards.

Happily there was no actual trouble, though the crowd was getting ugly, for, a little more than two hours later, there came the cheering news that a supporting gang of rescue workers had driven a new gallery through one of the pillars of coal, and that union with the old line was effected.

Again a faint rumble!

Hopes dropped once more, but, after a brief inspection, the mining engineer reported that the fall had taken place in another part of the mine and that there was no immediate danger.

At 8 o'clock that evening, voices could be faintly heard. An hour later, using a megaphone, the rescuers made the survivors hear that help was near them.

"How many of you are there?"

Thinly, so thinly that the voice could scarcely be heard, came back the answer:

"Three."

"All alive and well?"

"We are all alive. Jim Getwood and Anton Rover are unconscious. This is Clem Swinton talking."

"How is the air?"

"Getting bad, now."

"Keep your courage up! We'll have you out soon!"

The hewers set to work in high spirits, hoping that every blow of the pick would drive through.

Then:

"Stop work, men!" said the Bureau chief suddenly.

The men stared at him, amazed at the order. All stopped, however, except old Otto, who continued to use his pick-axe steadily.

The official grabbed him by the shoulder and spun him round with none too gentle a hand.

"Stop, you thick-head, when you're told!"

"What for? We'll be through this wall in an hour!"

"You'll have a hole through it, maybe. But what good will that do?"

Otto stared at the official amazed, and the Bureau of Mines man went on:

"You've had to start working in a respirator, after all, haven't you? Why? Because of white damp! Haven't you got sense enough to see what would happen as soon as you drove a hole through big enough to let the white damp in and not big enough to get the men out? How long do you think they'd last in this air, in their weakened state?"

Otto looked at him a moment, and then nodded his head.

"You're right, boss," he admitted. "I'm a fool. I'd never ha' thought o' that. But what are you goin' to do?"

"You don't seem to know enough to use your eyes," the official answered, shortly, "and they told me you were one of the best men in the mine! What do you suppose we've been doing all this cement construction along this gallery for the last couple of shifts?"

"I hadn't stopped to think," admitted Otto, taken aback.

"Well, you'll have a chance to do some thinking, now."

In effect, it was not surprising that Otto should not be able to see a way out of the difficulty, for the problem was a serious one.

The proportion of white damp, or carbon monoxide, in the air where the rescuers had now been compelled to work in respirators, was strong enough to kill a man in ten or fifteen minutes. In the undoubtedly weakened state of the three survivors, a lesser time than this would suffice to be fatal.

If, in the course of digging away the obstruction which remained between the rescuers and the entombed men, a small hole were made, or if the rocks should lie in such a manner that there were interstices between, Clem and his comrades would succumb before a sufficiently large breach could be made in the wall whereby they might be dragged through to liberty.

If, indeed, it were safe to blast, it might be possible to get rid of the obstruction by the use of a heavy blast and then rush through and grab the men. But this was impossible. The Burrell tester showed a large proportion of methane gas or fire damp, and a blast of any size might easily start an explosion which would not only wreck the mine, but also kill every member of the rescue parties, while affording no chance of getting the imprisoned men.

How could the wall be taken down, without allowing the gas to percolate through?

"Stand back, men," said the official, "here come the 'sand hogs,' now."

Amazed, the colliers retreated from the coal face to give place to a very different group of men. Small and wiry folk, these, dressed in an entirely different fashion from the miners. The respirators gave them the same goggle-eyed goblin faces. Not one of them had ever been in a coal mine before.

With a speed and dexterity that showed their knowledge of the work, these men proceeded to build up, at the side of the gallery, close to the point where the last obstruction still held, a solid face of concrete, and rapidly cemented it to the somewhat elaborate construction that had been in process of making all the preceding day, and to which Otto had paid no heed.

It was not long before it became evident that a completely closed room was being made. Other gangs came along, carrying strange screw-doors of iron, and a multitude of devices new to the eyes of miners. Everything had been measured and prepared above-ground. It remained only to throw the material together, according to a prearranged plan.

By midnight, all was ready.

Three "sand hogs," with a gallant young doctor who had volunteered, prepared to enter.

A steady throbbing sound told that machinery connected with an outlet pipe — solidly embedded in the cement — had been set in motion. The newly made walls threatened to bulge inwards, and the signal was given to stop.

Then a rushing noise was heard in the inlet pipe, similarly embedded. The outer of the double doors was opened and the four men stepped in, entering a tiny ante-chamber. They closed the outer door, which was absolutely air-tight, opened the inner one, and passed into the chamber built against the coal face, made of solid cement except for a circle of coal a yard in diameter.

A minute or two later, could be heard, faintly, the high screech of some rapid-cutting machine.

When Otto came back on his next shift, at 2 o'clock on Friday morning, the sand hogs were still working.

Curiosity overcame the old miner's desire not to seem ignorant.

"Just what is that, sir?" he asked the Bureau official, who was still on watch.

"That you, Otto? So you want to know, now, do you? Well, that's a sort of lightly made caisson, or air-tight chamber, with an air-lock or double door. It's used a good deal for working under water, but for the job we have here, it doesn't have to be very solidly built.

"It's simple enough, when you think it out. We just cemented it up, put in an air-pump to take out the gassy air that was in it, and then turned in compressed air, with a pressure of a little more than one atmosphere, just

48

enough to keep any of the gas from entering the hole that is being dug through the coal pillar."

"Why can't gas get in? Gas'll go through coal."

"Because the pressure from inside is bigger than from outside. The compressed air is leaking through the coal and driving any gas away."

"Why didn't you let us get in there to finish the job, if that's all there is to it?" protested Otto, indignant that strangers should have the glory of the final rescue, after the miners had done so much.

"Because you couldn't stand it. Those men are sand hogs. They're used to working in compressed air. Just as soon as a man gets into a pressure of two or three atmospheres, unless he's mighty careful he's apt to get dangerously ill. His blood absorbs too much air. While he's under compression, he doesn't feel it so much, but if he comes out of the compression too quickly, the surplus air in his blood can't come out as slowly as it ought, and little bubbles form in the blood current. That's deadly. Sometimes these bubbles cause a terrible caisson disease known as the 'bends,' when all the muscles and joints are affected; or it may give a paralysis known as 'diver's palsy,' because divers working in compressed atmospheres suffer the same way; all too often, it causes sudden death. So you see, Otto, it's not a chance a man ought to take who knows nothing about it."

"An' the sand hogs are diggin' in there?"

"No, they're not digging. We put in a tunnelling machine driven by compressed air, which is sometimes used for making sewers and the like. It will bore an even, round hole, just big enough for a man to crawl through, comfortably.

"As soon as that hole is pierced through into the room where the imprisoned men are, the doctor will go in, taking food, wine and medical supplies, and three respirators as well. Then, when the survivors are protected against the possible results of a sudden inrush of gas, it'll be up to you men to get the rest of the wall down as quick as you can."

"So that's how it is! We'll be ready, sir, as soon as you give the word."

At 6 o'clock, on the Friday morning, the outer door of the caisson clanged and the foreman of the sand hogs came out.

"We've pierced through," he said. "The doctor's in there. He says all the men are alive, as yet, but he doesn't know if they'll recover. There's not much time to lose, judging by what he says."

"At the wall, men!" came the order.

The miners cheered. They were to have the glory of getting their comrades out, after all.

The picks hammered on the rock like hail. The cars roared through the galleries once more. The cages shot upward with their loads.

At 8 o'clock, a miner's pick went through the wall into the space leading to the room beyond, but there was still a lot of rock to move before a clear passage could be made.

Otto remembered the warning of the Mine Bureau official, and realized that, had he been left to himself, he would have killed his comrades at the very moment of rescue.

At 9 o'clock, the hole was big enough for one of the rescuers to pass. As before, a doctor was the first to scramble through the opening.

The excitement above ground was enormous. Each car might bring a survivor!

Every time that the cage was a few seconds late, hope rose high.

"Keep silence, now," said the Mine Bureau's surgeon to the waiting crowd. "No cheers or shouts remember! The nerves of the men are apt to be at the breaking point."

The silence added to the tension. The atmosphere was electric with anxiety.

What was happening?

The cage was rising slowly, slowly!

Surely the men were there!

It reached the surface.

A limp form was borne out and laid on a waiting stretcher.

It was Anton, his face pinched, his lips blue.

In the next cage, Jim Getwood was brought up. On seeing his condition, the mine doctor shook his head dubiously. Artificial respiration was begun, then and there.

The cage rose for the third time, bearing Clem Swinton, unconscious like his comrades, but clearly in better case.

He stirred as he reached the open air, and his glance encountered that of the mine owner.

"I said American mine pluck would get us," he gasped, "if we stuck out long enough!"

And he relapsed into unconsciousness.

CHAPTER IV
EIGHT DAYS OF DARK

The three comrades were saved, indeed, but it was none too soon. Eight days below ground without food or light and without any sure hope of rescue, had brought them to a low ebb.

Clem, owing to his longer experience in the mine and his more prudent conserving of the scanty supply of food that fell to his share, had withstood the strain better than the two other survivors. He was badly shaken, however, and his nerves were on the edge of collapse. His efforts to help his companions had held him tense during those unending hours of darkness and famine, and his optimism had kept him from the ravages of despair.

Anton had received a terrible shock, both to body and mind. His hands and feet had become deadened, as though frozen, and the most vigorous treatment failed to restore the circulation. From time to time he was seized by convulsive fits; resembling those of epilepsy, and characteristic of white damp poisoning. His speech remained thick and mumbling, and he repeated the same word over and over, a score of times, without being conscious that he had spoken it.

Jim Getwood, the prospector, was in the weakest condition of the three. He lacked the degree of immunity that Clem possessed through his half-dozen years below ground, and that Anton possessed, in a minor degree, through heredity. His former life of adventure in the open air made him all the more susceptible to the poison gases. Violent headaches brought him to the verge of madness, and alternated with periods of delirium. He could retain little or no food, and, several times, the doctor despaired of saving his life.

Yet, in the history of coal-mining, there are several cases on record in which men have been even a longer time below ground and recovered. In a French colliery, two out of thirty men who were buried for fourteen days, recovered; in a Welsh colliery, one man survived out of seventy who had been entombed for seventeen days.

A still more astonishing case occurred in a Scotch coal-mine. A big roof-fall in a pit in Ayrshire had blocked off all the outlets to the shaft, save one, by which all the miners were able to escape. One man, however, finding that the way to the shaft was clear, returned to the face of the coal where he had been working, in order to get his coat.

On his way back to the shaft, a second fall occurred, blocking him in. This happened in 1835, when rescue work was still done in a primitive fashion. It was not until the twenty-third day that the miner was reached. He was alive, but in a dying state, his body being covered with a species of fungus that grows upon decaying mine timbers. He lived three days after being brought to the surface.

The longest record of endurance under such conditions occurred in France, some years later. A well-digger, near Lyons, was buried alive with a comrade, the sides of a deep well caving in after such a manner that an air-space of 37 feet was left above the entombed men.

It was impossible to try to remove the obstruction, for any effort to do so would only cause the earth and stones to fall on them and crush the men. In order to attempt rescue, it was necessary to sink a well as deep as the first, and, when the full depth was reached, to drive an underground gallery from one to the other.

Up to the very last day, the rescuers were able to hear tappings, sure sign that at least one of the men was alive. On the thirtieth day the rescue was effected. The oldest of the two well-diggers was found alive, but he was in a terrible condition because of the infection caused by the corpse of his comrade, who had died two weeks before. He, also, lived three days after his rescue, but the doctors were unable to save his life.

None of these men, however, had to withstand the effects of white damp in the air; on the other hand, none of them had any supply of food, however small, to begin with.

Clem's account of the experiences of the three men in the mine was awaited with a great deal of interest. Reporters from various newspapers hung around the mine for several days, waiting for a chance to get his story. The mine doctor refused permission, however, until he was assured that the young miner was well on his way to health, fearing that a reawakening of the memories of that terrible week might bring about a relapse. Finally he admitted the reporters to the hospital ward where the three survivors lay, though forbidding Anton and Jim to speak.

Clem was willing enough to tell his tale.

He began with the incident in the cage, on the morning of the accident, when he had joked with Otto, to the old miner's manifest objection. He told of Otto's refusal to work that day, according to the account given him by Jim. He described, also, how Anton had gallantly abandoned his own chance of safety to come and warn him, and explained how they had vainly searched an outlet in the direction of the North Gallery.

"Right after we met Jim," he went on, "we ran as fast as we could towards the old workings, to see if we could get out there. I didn't think there was much chance, because, so far as I could make out, the fall had happened between where we were working and the shafts. But it was worth trying, anyway. When we found the wall down, in that section, and the rock piled up clear to the roof, I knew we were trapped, sure.

"Thanks to what I had learned in the night-school classes, I had a pretty good idea of the general lay-out of the mine. I knew how the faults lay, and miners, who'd been in this mine a long time, had told me how gassy the old workings were.

"In a lesson I'd had on mine ventilation, we'd been told that the ventilating plant, here, had been enlarged twice over to try to keep the mine clear of gas. It wasn't hard to figure out that, with the ventilation stopped, gas would soon begin to collect, and that would be the end of us.

"There was a big-enough cap on our safety lamps, as it was, and it seemed to me that the blue cone grew longer as I looked. I told Jim that it wasn't safe for us to hang around those old workings, we'd get poisoned before we knew it and lose any chance we had of rescue.

"Jim didn't see it my way, at first.

"'Might as well die here as anywhere!' he said.

"I didn't like that spirit. I'd read in a book, somewhere, that if a chap gives up hope, he dies a whole lot quicker than if he keeps up his spirits. It was about Anton that I was worrying most. I was bent on trying to get the youngster cheerful if I could, because he was moping over Otto's prophecy that there was going to be an accident. You've heard about that, I suppose?"

The reporters nodded, and Owens, who was listening, added:

"We've heard a lot about it. The old man called the turn, all right. But maybe you don't know that he told me, too, that you'd be rescued and that you'd come out of it, alive?"

"Did he?" queried Clem, in amazement.

"Point-blank. It's a good thing for you he did, too, for a whole lot of first-class men volunteered for the rescue work who couldn't have been persuaded to enter the mine again, otherwise. The old man stuck to his belief, even after most of us thought you would be dead. The geophone expert backed him up, by saying he heard tapping, but it was Otto's persistence that did the most."

"It's a queer thing he should guess so closely," commented Clem thoughtfully.

But a reporter from a Pittsburgh evening paper, who was anxious to get the survivor's story on the telegraph wires, broke in impatiently:

"What was the first thing you did, after you'd found you were trapped?"

"We got busy and made a barricade," Clem answered. "I showed Jim and Anton that, in the old workings where we were, there was a lot of gas. Our lamps showed it up, good and strong. Now, back in the rooms where Jim and I had been hewing, there wasn't any gas to speak of. We could go back there, of course, and that was what Jim wanted to do.

"But I figured out that, since the ventilation was shut off from our rooms, the gas which had accumulated in the old workings and which was steadily seeping through the coal in that section would gradually creep along the galleries our way. If that happened, we'd be down and out, before the rescuers had a chance to cut their way through. We could put up a barricade, though, and cut off the gassy part of the mine.

"Jim didn't want to work, at first. If he was going to die, he said, he might as well die of gas as of hunger. He talked a lot of rot about its being the easiest death. I was that sore, I could have kicked him.

"Anton was willing enough to work, though, and when Jim saw the two of us actually at work, he got over his grouch, went and got his pick and shovel and slaved as hard as any of us. We piled up the coal and rock, good and thick, and then scraped up all the fine dust we could find and made a thick blanket of that to keep the gas from coming through, as best we could.

"Putting up that barricade made us mighty hungry. We were working fast because the gas there was bad, and we knew the quicker we got away from it, the better for us. Being hungry didn't do us much good. There wasn't much grub.

"We had only two pails of dinner, Jim's and mine. Anton's dinner pail was out by the entry where he took the loaded cars. So we pooled the food, and divided it into three exactly equal parts, each one of us to hide his share, and to eat it as quickly or as slowly as he pleased.

"Jim ate his at once, said he'd rather have one good meal than a lot of little bites which didn't mean anything. Anton made his last longer, he still had some food left when the lamps burned out. I only took a bite or two of mine, at that time, and managed to make eight meals of it, though, of course, I couldn't tell how many hours or days apart those meals were."

"How long did the safety-lamps burn?" asked the reporter.

"Eight hours after we were caught. They all went out within a few minutes of each other—and we had them pretty well turned down, too. I looked at my watch, just as the last one flickered out. It wasn't quite a quarter past eight."

"You had no matches?" the reporter asked.

"Matches? What a fool idea!" exclaimed Clem, amazed at the reporter's ignorance. "I should say not! Even the lamps are locked. We could have had light three times as long, if it wasn't for that, burning first one and then the other, but there's no way to light a lamp below ground.

"Before the lamps went out, each of us had scraped up a pile of coal dust to sleep on. It was plenty warm down there, and getting warmer all the time. The lack of air made us all heavy and drowsy. We were all asleep pretty soon after the lamps went out.

"We woke up in the dark. It was black as pitch, a blackness which weighed on you. It hurt. One's eyes wanted to fight against it.

"How long had we been asleep? An hour, ten hours, or the whole twenty-four? Not one of us could tell.

"But the sleep had done one good thing. It had helped Jim a lot. He was full of pep, again. The old prospecting optimism had come back. He was dead sure that he could find a way out. All it needed was looking for, he thought.

"Anton wasn't awake yet, and I didn't want to wake him up. The longer he slept, the better. I tried to reason with Jim that we'd already gone to all the openings there could be, but he wouldn't listen to reason. He wouldn't stay with us. He was restless. He just had to be up and wandering.

"'How are you going to find your way back?' I asked him. 'It's easy to get lost in the dark, and you don't know much about the mine.'

"'I'll be back with a full dinner-pail while you're sitting there doing nothing!' he boasted, and off he started. I'd have gone with him, quick enough, but I didn't want Anton to wake and find himself alone.

"After a while Anton woke up. I heard him munching, so I knew he was at his grub. I warned him not to finish it all at once, but he was so hungry he couldn't stop. I couldn't blame him much, at that. I was so ravenous that my stomach seemed to be tying itself up in knots, and the flesh inside seemed to crawl.

"I had to tell him that Jim had gone off by himself. Anton didn't say much to that. In fact, he didn't want to talk at all. He was brooding all the time. Twice I overheard him muttering to himself, and both times he was talking about Otto and his warning.

"I could see he was blaming me, but I'll say this for the boy — he never once said that he regretted having come back to warn me."

"That," interrupted the superintendent emphatically, "shows the boy is good stuff. It takes a good deal of moral courage to keep from blaming some one else, when you're in a pinch. I remember, once, in West Australia — " He checked himself. "Go ahead with your story, lad."

Clem resumed.

"Some time after — it seemed about an hour, though it may have been a good deal less or a good deal more — we heard shouting.

"'Jim's found the way out!' cried Anton, and scrambled to his feet.

"I grabbed him as he rose.

"'Don't run off in that fool fashion,' I said to him. 'Make sure where the shouts are coming from, first. You've been down in a mine long enough to know that the echoes are apt to make a noise sound as if it comes in a directly opposite direction from the right one.'

"'I'm going to find Jim!' he insisted.

"'If you must run chances, why, I suppose you must,' said I. 'But I'm going to stay here, where the air's good. Try to get back here. Keep in touch. You take ten paces forward, then stop and shout. I'll answer. If you don't hear me, come back.'

"He promised and started off. For the first fifty yards or so — supposing that he shouted at every ten paces — I heard him clear enough.

"Then — not another sound! What had happened to him?

"I shouted again and again.

"No reply!

"What was I going to do? Both Jim and Anton were wandering around loose in the mine galleries, and they might stray until they dropped, without ever finding the way back. I yelled till I was hoarse.

"Then I got another idea. I took my pick, and kept on hitting the roof in three regular strokes: 'Tap! Tap! Tap!' and then a pause—just like that." He illustrated on the head-rail of his hospital bed. "I knew that the vibration would carry along the rock, farther than the voice."

"That's what the geophone man heard," Owens commented to the reporter. "Go on, lad!"

"I kept that up," Clem went on, "until my arms ached. I was so tired in my back and so weak with hunger that bright violet spots kept dancing before my eyes. But I kept on, just the same.

"Then I heard a shout, and, presently, Anton came staggering along, dead beat. He'd been guided back by the sound of the tapping.

"'No sign of Jim?' I asked

"'Nothing!'

"He lay down on the coal dust, and, pretty soon, I heard him breathing hard. He'd gone right off to sleep, exhausted, poor kid!"

"How long do you suppose he'd been wandering?" queried the reporter.

"No way of knowing. But I'm pretty husky, and I can stand an eight hours' shift of coal hewing without getting too tired. And, I tell you, I was about done out, just from reaching up and tapping that roof with a pick. Of course, I was weak. But I reckon it must have been eight hours, good, that the youngster was straying in those mine galleries, in the dark, alone. Maybe it was more.

"I must have gone to sleep, too, but it didn't seem for long. Half-asleep, I heard Anton say,

"'There's a rat gnawing at my stomach!'

"I woke up right quick, at that, for though mine rats are ugly customers, I thought if we could catch a rat or two, that might give us food. But what the boy meant was that he was so hungry that it felt as if a rat were there.

"I wasn't exactly hungry, leastways, not all the time. The pain came in cramps, that were bad enough while they lasted, but I didn't feel anything much between. My tongue was getting swollen, though. I knew what that meant. Drink of some sort we must have.

"'Look here, Anton,' I said, 'you tap on the rock, in threes, the same as I did, and I'll go try to find water. I know the lay-out of this mine better than you do, and there used to be a sump (hole) near the goaf (waste rock taken from the main gallery roofs). Maybe there'll be water there.'

"I started off, cheerfully enough. I reckoned I knew the mine. So I do, with a lamp, but I didn't have any idea what it meant to wander in the pitch-dark. The galleries were low there, too, not more than four feet high. I had to keep one hand stretched out in front of me to keep from going headlong into the wall, and the dinner pail that I was carrying in that hand struck the side more times than I could count; I kept the other hand above my head, to keep me from cracking my skull against the cross-timbers holding up the low roof.

"Before I'd gone a hundred yards, I was so mixed up that I didn't know which way I was going or where I'd come from. It's a horrible feeling. The dark is like a trap that you can't feel and you can't see, but you know it's there. It's being blind with your eyes open.

"Then it was so ghastly silent, too. A blind man can always hear something. There's life around him. Down there, not a sound! I'd lost all hearing of the 'Tap! Tap! Tap!' I'd told Anton to make.

"All sorts of nasty things came into my head. I might step into a hole and get crippled. I might walk straight into a pocket of gas, and, without any safety lamp to tell me of the danger, be poisoned then and there. The roof might be bulging down, right over my head, ready to fall and I'd have no warning.

"I tried to reason it out that all these ideas were just imagination. Reasoning didn't do much good. Fright got a grip of me. I was in a cold sweat all over. My heart thumped so that it hurt. I was just horribly scared, right through, and I had to bite my lips till they were raw to keep from screaming.

"I'd have gone under, sure, if I'd been alone, but I had the kid to think of, and every time the tin dinner pail banged against the wall, it reminded me of what I'd come to look for. Anton would die of thirst in a few hours, if I didn't find water. As for Jim, I reckoned he was probably done for, anyway.

"I think—I'm not sure but I think so—I had a spell of running crazily round and round in a circle, trying to get away from something—I don't know what. It was then I gave my head a bang," he pointed to the bandage still on his head, "and while that stunned me a bit, it steadied me, too.

"By that time, I was lost for fair. I couldn't hear Anton's tapping. I couldn't hear anything. I tried to turn back and got all mixed up in the run of the galleries. I wandered this way and that, as blindly as if I'd never been in the mine before.

"And then I heard a sound like the ticking of a big clock.

"That scared me more than anything.

"I remembered all Otto's' stories about the 'knockers,' and, though I didn't believe them, I couldn't get them out of my head. Somebody, something, was knocking softly underground!

"It wasn't human, that was sure!

"It couldn't be Anton, because he'd been told to tap in threes. It couldn't be Jim, for the ticks were too close together to be the strokes of a pick; besides, I knew that Jim had left his tools behind. It couldn't be rescuers, because the sound was near me. Near me? It was almost at my ear.

"Sometimes breaking timber cracks. It might be a prop gradually giving way, I thought, just ready to let down a new fall of rock on my head. But a creaking timber is sometimes loud, sometimes soft, and this ticking, as I said, was regular, like a big clock.

"Then I guessed!

"It was drops of water falling!

"I could have shouted with relief, but down there, in the dark and the stillness, the silence was so heavy that I was afraid to shout.

"I felt my way forward, one step and then a second, and the ticking stopped.

"I took a third step and it began again. I stepped backward, and a little to one side, and the drop fell on my bare shoulder.

"I took my dinner-pail, moved it forward, backward, this way and that, until at last I heard the drops falling in the tin.

"I was too thirsty to wait long. As soon as there was a teaspoonful of water in the pail, I moistened my tongue with it. That was a relief! I was able to hold out the tin pail, the next time, until there was a reasonable drink.

"Ugh, it was bitter! It tasted coppery and twisted up my mouth, but it was liquid, at least. After I had a drink or two, I felt better. My scare passed away.

"Then I began to think a bit. If water was dropping as quickly as that, it must be running somewhere. But where? I got down on my hands and knees and began to feel along the floor. Here it was damp; there, dry. I crawled along for a few minutes, following the line of the damp floor, and, sure enough, came to a hollow where a good-sized puddle had collected. There I was able to half-fill the pail.

"So far, I was all right. I'd found the water. But how was I to get back to Anton? And where was Jim, if he were still alive? I hadn't any idea, any more, of which way to turn.

"Then I got a scheme. Suppose I just walked straight ahead, keeping my right hand against the wall, and turning to the right at every opening I came to? I knew that we were hemmed in at every point. Therefore, I figured, we must be inside some kind of an irregular circle. The place where we had made our beds was in the room where I had been working, which was in the end gallery, and, at that rate, somewhere on the circumference of that circle. If I kept on going, long enough, I'd be bound to strike the place.

"Off I started with the pail half-full of water. I walked, in and out, up one gallery and down another, coming back to the rock falls which had blocked the way, and on again. I tried to count my paces, and, though I forgot sometimes, I figured that I'd done about seven thousand paces when I heard, faintly:

"'Tap! Tap! Tap!'

"It seemed to come from behind me.

"I wasn't to be fooled by the echoes, though, and so I kept on as I had been going. Just a little further and I turned a corner and came to the place where we had made our beds.

"Anton was down.

"He hadn't been able to keep on tapping on the roof, as I had told him to. He hadn't the strength. But the kid's pluck was holding, though his vitality wasn't. He'd taken his maul (a large hammer used for driving wedges in the coal) and was lifting this from the ground and then dropping it, three strokes at a time, like I'd told him to do.

"When I spoke to him he couldn't answer. His tongue was so swollen that it just about filled up his whole mouth.

"I gave him some water, a sip or two at a time, and then, when I thought he could stand it, a real drink. Even then, I had to go slow, for my dinner pail was only half-full.

"I still had a few bites of food left, but I wasn't hungry, I'd gone too far for that. My mouth was sore, too. The copperas water screwed up my palate and my tongue like eating unripe bananas does, only a lot worse. It worked the same way on Anton."

"It was that water that helped you, though," put in the mine doctor. "The sulphate of iron in it lowered the activity of the body, drying it up, so that you could go on with less loss of tissue."

"It tasted nasty enough to have anything in it! Just the same, it was water. When I woke up from a nap, I found the pail empty. The youngster had finished it, but when I rowed him for doing it, he couldn't remember having drunk it at all. He was only half-conscious, any way.

"My tongue was beginning to swell again. I saw we'd have to shift our headquarters so as to be near that water, or the time would come when we'd be too weak to go hunting it. So, following the same scheme of making a whole circle of the part of the mine where we were trapped, I went back the way I'd come, making sure that Anton was following right behind me.

"It seemed a whole lot farther off than I'd thought, I suppose because I was afraid of passing the place. After a couple of hours, though, I heard the sound of the dropping water. It was great to hear it again! We took some long drinks there, I can tell you. Then we scooped up with our hands some coal dust to lie on, and slumped down again. I was beginning to feel pretty weak."

"About what day do you suppose that was?" the reporter asked.

"I haven't any idea. Sometimes I thought we'd only been down there a few hours, sometimes it seemed like weeks. I suppose, really, it was about the third or the fourth day.

"I woke up suddenly.

"Somebody was laughing!

"It was a queer high-pitched laugh, and half-choked, something like the neighing of a horse.

"Anton heard it, too.

"'The knockers are coming for us!' he said to me, hoarsely. 'It's just like Father said. They're laughing at us!'

"Well, I don't mind telling you my blood ran a bit cold. I'm not superstitious, but, for the second time in that mine, I was scared enough to run. But where to?

"Anton was gasping horribly; it made me worse to hear him. I put my hand on his shoulder to quiet him. He was trembling and shaking, like as he had a chill.

"The laughing came nearer, and louder.

"The louder it got, the less I was scared. After the first few seconds of fright, I got all right again, and started to think quietly. Then the real reason came to me.

"It must be Jim!

"I let out a loud shout.

"The laughing stopped dead.

"Then I knew it was Jim; things that weren't human wouldn't care if I shouted or not.

"'Keep quiet!' I said to Anton. 'It's Jim, and he's coming this way.'

"Presently the laughter began again, a sort of half choked scream, like I said, but it was laughing just the same. It made my flesh creep to hear it. Somehow it wasn't quite human, more like an animal trying to laugh like a man.

"It was quite close to us, now. I got up, for I could hear steps shuffling along the gallery.

"Suddenly, something bumped into me, though I thought the steps were several yards away.

"It was Jim, sure enough.

"He gave a sort of screech and both his hands went up to my throat, in a strangling grip.

"I'm a good deal bigger than Jim, but I was like a baby in his hands. He had me like in a vise.

"'Help! Help! Anton!' I called. 'He's throttling me! It's Jim!'

"At that, the kid got up, tottering. He was weak enough, but, as you know, he's really got muscles of iron. In spite of his scare—for he was dead sure that it was something supernatural—he came to my help.

"The minute he got his hands on Jim and found that it was really flesh and blood that he was tackling, and not any sort of goblin, he got furious. He wrenched at his opponent savagely, and the more furious he got, the more his strength came back. I could hear his sinews cracking.

"But Jim's grip was that of a madman.

"It was a good thing for me that Anton was the son of the champion wrestler of the mine. Despite his powerful muscles, he could do nothing, absolutely nothing against the madman. I felt him let go, and thought that was the end. My head was bursting, my heart fluttering.

"Then, with a swift change of hold, the youngster took Jim in a wrestler's grip, one he had learned from his father. It's a death hold, unless the other weakens. I heard Jim gasp. The clutch loosened. At last I could breathe and I shook myself free.

"But the madman was not tamed. His fists shot out like flails. One blow took Anton full in the chest. I heard his body crash against the wall. I could do little to help him, that choking grip had taken away every ounce of force I had.

"There wasn't any need for my help. That blow had roused Anton to a rage but little less than that of his mad foe. He knew nothing of boxing, but he could wrestle. It was a grim fight, down there in the dark!

"Despite the madman's blows, Anton ran in, clutched him in some kind of a wrestler's grip, lifted him clear off his feet and threw him over his shoulder.

"The madman fell heavily on the rock floor and lay like a log.

"For a minute or two we panted, saying nothing. Then,

"'Have you killed him, Anton?' I asked.

"'I don't know. I hope so,' he answered savagely.

"I felt pretty much that way, myself, at first, for my throat felt as if it were twisted clear out of shape. But, as I began to feel a bit better, I thought of Jim lying there.

"After all, he hadn't had any water! Small wonder he'd gone mad.

"Staggering—for that grip had nearly done for me—I got over beside him and knelt down. His heart was still beating, pretty rapidly, at that. But his jaws were almost locked upwards, forced apart by his thickened and swollen tongue.

"I got some water into his mouth, but with difficulty. I couldn't pry his tongue down far enough to get more than a drop or two in. But I kept at it—hours, I reckon—and kept on giving him sips of water until he began to breathe a bit more naturally.

"Then I reckon I fainted, for, when I came to, I was lying right across Jim. He was still unconscious, but the tongue was a whole lot better and he was nearly able to close his mouth. I poured a lot more water into him. Then I tried to give him a bite from the bread I had left, but he couldn't swallow. So I gave it to Anton, who was moaning a good bit.

"Me, I was getting less and less hungry. The gnawing pain that I'd felt at the beginning, especially that first time that I was hunting water, only came back at longer and longer intervals. In between, I felt quite all right, rather jolly, in fact. I caught myself laughing, once, the way I'd heard Jim, and I had hard work to stop it. Hysterical, I reckon.

"I must have slept a lot, or fainted, I don't know which. I remember having dreamed that I was rescued, oh, a score of times! Always, when I was asleep, there seemed plenty of light, generally a bright violet. It was only when I woke up that it was dark. The blackness was like a rock lying on my chest. The air I breathed seemed to taste black.

"Jim got violent, more than once. To end up, I had to tie his feet with my belt, so he couldn't get up on his feet. I wasn't going to risk any more fights like we'd had with him at the start.

"When he wasn't struggling, he was talking. He talked nearly all the time, and mostly about some gold mine that he'd found, that he knew would make him a millionaire and that he wanted to go back to. He described the place, over and over again. I believe I could go right there, just from hearing him. The only thing that quieted him was when I answered. Then he'd shut right up, only to begin again, after a while.

"What worried me the most about Jim was that he couldn't keep the bitter water on his stomach. He'd vomit it up, almost as soon as I'd get it down. I kept pouring it into him, just the same.

"When I put the last bite of grub into Anton—he was dead unconscious—it seemed like the end of everything. I lost all track of time. I don't know what happened, after that. I got quite light-headed, I think.

"Half the while, I didn't know whether the time I was dreaming was real, or the time I was awake. I knew somehow that the air was getting bad, and I remember thinking that this might be because a rescue party was trying to get down the wall.

"But there was always plenty of light when I was asleep, and I liked that, so, every time I was awake, I tried to go back to sleep."

"Didn't you hear any sounds of the rescue party coming nearer?" Owens asked.

"I heard them all the time, even when they weren't there," Clem answered. "How was I to tell what was real and what was dream?

"On one side was Jim telling about his gold mine, on the other was Anton, crying out from time to time that the knockers had him. Poor kid, he seemed to be in a nightmare all the while."

"But when the rescuers first spoke to you," the owner of the mine suggested, "you answered naturally enough."

"Perhaps I did, but I don't remember hearing them, at all, and I don't remember answering, at least, not more than I had a dozen times before. I'm not sure that I remember when the doctor came in and put a gas mask on me. It's all sort of vague.

"The first thing I do remember was coming up to the top and seeing a green tree. The trees weren't green when I went down a week ago, and I hadn't dreamed about trees, at all.

"Right now, it's hard to realize that I was buried down there for a week. If I wasn't so feeble, I'd think it was only a nightmare."

"And about this gold mine of Jim's," queried the reporter, scenting another phase of the story. "What was that?"

Jim, in a neighboring bed, half-raised himself in anxiety, but his comrade threw him a reassuring look.

"You'll have to ask Jim that, when he gets better," Clem answered. "I can't give away his secret. It might be true!"

CHAPTER V
THE LURE OF GOLD

In Clem's story one word had been spoken, the one word which, in all ages, has been as a raging fire in men's minds, which has sent scores to die on the scorching deserts of Africa and Australia, or on the borders of the Arctic Seas, which has bred fevered adventure, lawlessness, and murder wherever it has been spoken, the word:

Gold!

Many years had passed since Owens had felt this auriferous fever, many years since his heart had beat impetuously as in the wild days of the camps of his youth, but the word had rung again in his ears as of old. The subtle poison of the lure was in his veins once more. He could not sleep for thinking of the old prospector lying almost at the point of death in his own mine hospital, and, perhaps, dying with the secret of millions, untold.

He reasoned with himself for his foolishness. Over and over again he reminded himself that he was settled for life as a colliery-owner, and that coal mines bring far more wealth than gold mines have ever done. The spell was stronger than his reason. Night after night he sat late in his library, reading anew the lore of gold that he had once known so well, and dreaming avid visions over the pages.

The records of human daring do not reach so far back in the dawn of history as to show a time when gold was not a goal. In the earliest laws as yet known—the Laws of Menes in Egypt, B. C. 3000—both gold and silver were sought and used as standards of value in the royal and priestly treasuries. Breastplates and ornaments of gold were buried with the mummies of kings and nobles of Egypt and Mycenae.

There was gold in Chaldea and Armenia. The fable of Tantalus, who kept unlawful possession of a golden dog which had been stolen from Zeus, the great All-Father, was a legend of the gold placer deposits near Mt. Sipylus, north of Smyrna. The earliest records show a knowledge of gold in the Caucasus, Ural, and Himalaya Mts.

The Phœnicians, most adventurous of all the early races, went on long expeditions to distant lands in search of gold. Cadmus, the Phœnician, in B. C. 1594, sent miners to Thrace and established a regular gold-trade thence. As a curious forecast of what was to happen on the other side of the world, tens of centuries later, the ancient historian Strabo tells of a wagon-wheel uncovering a nugget of gold near Mt. Pangeus, not far from the present Bulgarian frontier.

One of the oldest of all the tales of high adventure was the Quest of the Golden Fleece, and the fifty heroes who set out on that quest in the oared ship Argo—and hence called the Argonauts—have given their name to gold-seekers for hundreds of generations. Few tales in all the world are so wonderful as the old Greek legend of Jason and the Golden Fleece, a quest of daring, of magic, and of peril.

The Golden Fleece, itself, was a thing of mystery. Its origin harks back to the earliest days of the Age of Fable. Thus, in its briefest form, runs the tale:

In a minor kingdom of what is now Northern Greece, there lived a king, Athamas, son of the god of the sea, who had married Nephele, the goddess of the clouds. But Athamas proved faithless and fell in love with Ino, grand-daughter of Aphrodite, the goddess of love and beauty. The cloud-goddess, indignant at this neglect, disappeared, leaving behind her two children, Phrixus and Helle.

It was not long before the stepmother conceived a violent hatred for the children of the first wife. Counting on the spell of her beauty, she tried to persuade Athamas to get rid of them, but the king refused. Then Ino fell to base plotting. She brought about a famine in the land by secretly heating the grains of wheat before they were sown and thus preventing their growth; then, by a false oracle, she persuaded the king that the gods were angry and would only be appeased if he offered his eldest-born, Phrixus, as a sacrifice. For the sake of his country, the king agreed.

All was in readiness, Phrixus was on the altar, the officiating priest had the knife raised, when masses of cloud and fog rolled over the scene and Nephele appeared, leading a ram with a fleece all threads of gold. So thick was the fog, that, in an instant, it blotted out all vision; the priest's hand stayed uplifted, for he could no longer see his victim to deal the fatal blow. Then came a rift in the fog, and, through the swirl of mist, Athamas and Ino saw Phrixus and his sister leap upon the back of the gold-fleeced ram.

Down the mountain and across the plain the great ram sped, and plunged into the waters of the strait that lies between Europe and Asia Minor, breasting the waves with ease. Helle fell from the back of the ram and was drowned, so that the strait (now known as the Dardanelles) was known to the Greeks as the Hellespont.

Phrixus reached the other side in safety. Following the counsel of his cloud-mother, he sacrificed the ram to the honor of the gods and took the fleece to Æetes, king of Colchis. Æetes at first received him with honor, but later proved false to his promises of friendship and made Phrixus a prisoner. The Golden Fleece was hung up on a tree in the grove of Ares (god of battle and grandfather of Ino), and there the mystic treasure was guarded by a dragon which never slept.

Now Pelias, brother of Athamas, had usurped the throne of Thessaly. When Jason, son of the true king, Aeson, had grown to man's estate, he presented himself before Pelias and challenged him to surrender the kingdom.

The wily Pelias, knowing well that the people of Thessaly would side with Jason, did not refuse outright. He demanded, only, that Jason should show his rightfulness to be deemed a king's son by some act of heroic bravery. Such a test was not unusual in the Days of Fable, and Jason agreed.

"This will I do," said Jason, "name the deed!"

Cunningly the king answered,

"Bring me the Golden Fleece!"

Jason, high-hearted, set out on the quest. Since he must cross the sea, there must be built a ship. Through the advice of the cloud-goddess, his mother, he appealed for help to Athene, goddess of wisdom, and a bitter enemy of Ares and his grand-daughter Ino. The fifty-oared ship Argo was built, and Athene herself placed in the prow a piece of oak endowed with the power of speaking oracles.

The Quest of the Golden Fleece was a deed worthy of heroes, and none but heroes were members of the crew. Such men — demigods, most of them — had never been gathered in a crew before. Orpheus, of the charmed lyre; Zetes and Calaïs, sons of the North Wind; Castor and Pollux, the divine Twins; Meleager, the hunter of the magic boar; Theseus, the slayer of tyrants; the all-powerful Hercules, son of Zeus, whose twelve labors were famous in all antiquity; and others of little lesser fame, were numbered in that gallant company.

Many and strange were their adventures in the Argo, of which there is not space to tell. The tale is one of ever-increasing wonder: the battle with the Harpies, evil birds with human heads; the peril of the Sirens, whose deadly singing was drowned by Orpheus' song; the menace of the Symplegades, or moving rocks, which clashed together when a ship passed between; the fight with the Stymphalian birds, who used their feathers of brass as arrows; and many more. The story of the voyage of the Argo is a story that will never die.

Despite their wanderings and their adventures, the Quest of the Golden Fleece remained the goal of the Argonauts. After months — or it may have been years — Jason and the heroes reached the land they sought. There they presented themselves before Æetes and demanded the Golden Fleece.

The king of Colchis looked at these heroes and trembled. Well he knew that neither he nor his people were a match for such as they. He took refuge in stratagem, and, as Pelias had done, demanded from Jason the performance of feats he deemed impossible. He must yoke and tame the bulls of Hephæstus, god of fire, which snorted flame and had hoofs of red-hot brass; with these he must plow the field of Ares, god of battle; that done, he must sow the field with dragon's teeth, from which a host of armed men would spring, and he must defeat that army.

Truly, the task was one to tax a hero. But, as the gods would have it, Jason found a new but dangerous ally. This was Medea, the witch-daughter of Æetes, grand-daughter of Helios, god of the sun. She loved her father but little, for her father had imprisoned her for sorcery and, though she had escaped by means of her black arts, her dark heart brooded vengeance.

Partly from love of Jason and partly from hatred of Æetes, she leagued herself with the heroes.

Jason was not proof against her wiles. Moreover, he realized that the task Æetes had set him was one almost beyond the doing. He accepted from the dark witch-maiden a magic draught which made him proof against fire and sword. Thus, scorning alike the fiery breath of the bulls and the myriad blades of the tiny swordsmen, he plowed the field of Ares and sowed it with the dragon's teeth. Then he threw a charm among the ranks of the dwarf warriors who sprang up from the soil, which caused them to fight, one against the other, until all were slain. Thus he reached the wood where hung the Golden Fleece.

There remained still to be conquered the dragon that never slept. Again the sorceress Medea came to the hero's help. By wild witch songs she charmed the monster to harmlessness, and, stepping across the snaky coils, Jason snatched from a bough the Golden Fleece, won at last!

Though the Argonauts feared Medea, and though Jason dreaded her fully as much as he was lured by her, the heroes could not deny that their quest had been successful mainly through her aid. For her reward, Medea demanded that they take her back to Greece in the Argo, and she took her young brother Absyrtus, with her. The oracle of oak in the bow prophesied disaster, but the heroes had pledged their words and could not retract.

The Argo had not gone far upon the sea before the heroes saw that Æetes was pursuing them. Here was a peril, truly, for Ares, god of battle, was on the pursuer's side. Then Medea seized her young brother, cut his body into pieces and scattered them on the sea. The anguished father stopped to collect the fragments and to return them to the shore for honorable burial. By this shameful device, the Argonauts escaped.

So hideous a crime demanded a dreadful expiation, but Jason was to draw the doom more directly upon his own head. Though he had shuddered at the murder of Absyrtus and he knew the witch-maid's hands were red with blood, the spell of Medea's dark beauty overswept his loathing. At the first land where the Argo stopped, he married her.

At this the gods were little pleased. They sent a great darkness and terrible storms which drove the Argonauts over an unknown sea to lands of new and fearful perils. Once they were all but swallowed in a quicksand, again, menaced by shipwreck, a third time, a giant whose body was of brass threatened them with a hideous death from which they were saved only by the twins, Castor and Pollux. The homeward journey of the Argo was not less wild and difficult than her coming.

Yet, at the last, Jason brought back the Golden Fleece to Thessaly, only to find that the false Pelias had slain Aeson and Jason's mother and brother during the absence of the Argonauts. His crime was not left unpunished. Medea persuaded the daughters of Pelias to cut their father into small pieces and to boil the fragments in a pot with certain witch-herbs that she gave them, falsely promising that by this means the old king would regain his youth. Of the later life of Jason and Medea, there is no need to speak. Misery was their lot, and their deaths were not long delayed.

Thus, in fanciful guise, appears in the old Greek legend the record of the European discovery of the alluvial gold deposits of Colchis, and to the Argonauts was ascribed the honor of being the first to bring to Greece the gold of Asia Minor. Even in those early days, the gift of gold was regarded as the favor of the gods.

There is good reason to believe that the Siege of Troy—the subject of Homer's Iliad—was not waged alone because of the beauty of Helen of Troy, but also because the Greeks coveted Mycenæan gold. Excavations made on the site of ancient Troy have revealed many thin plates of beaten gold.

Nor was the Argo the only ship to set sail to unknown lands for gold. As early as the fabled voyage of the Argonauts, or even earlier, Queen Hatshepsut of Egypt—a mighty woman monarch of whom all too little is known—sent an expedition to Punt (possibly Somaliland) for incense and for gold. On the walls of the great temples built during her reign are found paintings telling the story of this expedition, picturing, among other things, the bags of gold that the three-masted, thirty-oared ship brought home.

Hiram, King of Tyre, who was engaged by King Solomon to bring treasures for the Temple at Jerusalem, made a long journey to some distant land (about B. C. 1000) and, after having been three years away, brought back gold and silver, as well as ivory, apes, and peacocks. He certainly went to India and may have visited Peru.

The Phrygians were known not only as miners of gold but also as workers in the precious metal. The "golden sands of Pactolus" were washed a thousand years before the Christian era. The proverbial wealth of Crœsus and the legend of the "golden touch of Midas" remain as historic memories of the gold mines of Asia Minor and Arabia, worked by the Lydian kings.

When Persia became the mistress of the world, most of this gold was taken to the courts of Cyrus, Cambyses, and Darius. Some of it, but not all, came back in the victorious train of Alexander the Great, when ten thousand teams of mules and five hundred camels were required to carry the treasure to the new world capital at Susa.

Spain, in addition to Egypt and Arabia, became one of the principal gold-bearing sources of the ancient world. The Carthaginians, colonists from Phœnicia, conquered the Iberians, who then populated Spain, and forced them to work in gold mines. They captured negroes and shipped them to Spain as slaves in the gold diggings. The Carthaginians also exploited mines in Sicily, Sardinia, and Corsica.

Then Rome, rising into power, cast covetous eyes on the gold possessed by Carthage, and sought to seize it by force of arms. As a result of her victory in the First Punic (Carthaginian) War, Rome secured the three islands of the Mediterranean, rich in minerals.

The Carthaginians, under the leadership of Hannibal, worked the mines of Spain and Portugal the harder. The rivers Douro and Tagus were found to be rich in gold-bearing sands. Rome's envy grew. In the Second Punic War, she captured Spain. From the gold-mines there, worked by slave labor, came a large share of the riches and luxury of the Roman Empire.

To Owens, sitting in his library in an American colliery town, the long story of civilization seemed to unroll before his eyes and, everywhere, possession of gold brought power and fame. In every case, also, that same possession led to luxury and decline.

When Rome fell, beneath the impact of the barbarian hordes, the Byzantine Empire, holding the gold-mines of Macedonia, Thrace, and Asia Minor, rose to a bought magnificence. It crumbled easily, because it depended on gold to buy its mercenary armies, even as Carthage had crumbled before Rome.

The same story was repeated in the Saracenic power, when the Caliphates of Bagdad and of Damascus rose to that wealth of which the "Arabian Nights" gives a picture. The mines of Arabia, Egypt, and Spain were in their hands, and the luxury of such Moorish towns as Granada was made possible by the final workings of the almost exhausted alluvial deposits of Spain. It was not until the days of Ferdinand and Isabella of Castile that the Moors were conquered, and, in those days, Cortés tapped the gold-stores of Mexico, and Pizarro, those of Peru.

As ever, the gold of the Aztecs and the Incas, ruthlessly seized so soon after the voyages of Columbus, made Spain the mistress of the world. While the Conquistadores were fighting, Spain remained strong. When the gold was acquired, Spain began to fall.

England was a frugal country, then. But, like Rome, as soon as her neighbor began to acquire vast stores of gold, she sought a pretext for a war. English pirates and privateers commenced to harry the treasure-ships of Spain, to plunder the Spanish settlements in America, and to sack every town that was thought to contain American gold. Upon this stolen treasure, England rose to wealth and power, as did also Holland and France, the three nations having made a naval alliance for greed of Spanish gold.

Nor was England content with her ill-gotten gains. Through commercial companies which only thinly disguised colonization projects, she sought possession of gold-bearing regions. The gold of India, of Australia, and of South Africa, changed the Kingdom of England into the British Empire, during the reign of a single queen. No one will seriously dispute that the annexation of the Transvaal and even the Boer War of recent years were based on England's desire to control the enormous gold resources of the Rand, as well as the diamond fields.

The gold history of the United States is little less striking. The Louisiana Purchase was based largely on the mineral wealth known to exist in that territory, the annexation of California and her rise to statehood were built on gold. The purchase of Alaska in 1867 was largely due to the discovery of gold in British Columbia in 1857, 1859 and 1860, and to the discoveries on the Stikine River, Alaska, in 1863.

The 146 years of life of the United States may be sharply divided into two equal periods, that before the discovery of gold in California in 1848 and the period following. The amazing strides forward which the United States has made during this last period are not to be ascribed only to her virgin soil, to her geographic isolation, or to her form of government, but more, a thousand times more, to her mining development. Coal, iron, silver, copper, and above all—gold, opened up the continent with passionate swiftness and hurled the United States into the position of one of the great powers of the modern world.

So Owens sat a-thinking in his library and racking his brain about Jim. There, not a stone's throw away, lay a sick man, possibly possessed of a secret that might change the face of history anew.

How many times it had happened that a lonely prospector, weary, ragged and hungry, had, with a stroke of a pick or the flick of a pan, revealed such sources of wealth as to change a burning desert, a fetid swamp or a bleak mountain range into a hive of industry! What statesman has ever wrought as many wonders for his country as has that questing nomad with his shovel and his shallow pan?

The spirit of rugged honesty and of fair play which so sharply distinguishes the real miner from the mere mining speculator lay deep in Owens. He had worked in the gold diggings, himself, and his standards of principle were those of the great outdoors. He scorned to take advantage of the opportunity given him by his position as owner of the mine to overhear the delirious ravings of the sick man. That he might not be tempted, he kept away from the hospital ward, except for a short daily visit of inquiry.

When Jim grew better, however, and evinced a marked liking for Owens' company, the mine-owner yielded to his interest in the prospector. Even then he restrained himself from making so much as an indirect reference to the secret of his employe, though the matter was seldom out of his mind.

He had no thought of filching Jim's secret from him. Honest to the core, Owens' thoughts were on a larger scale. As a mining man, he thought naturally what personal profit he could turn, should the secret prove to be worth while; but he thought far more of Jim. He rejoiced in the hope that, perhaps, he could bring to fulfilment the prospector's hidden dream. And, most of all, he wished to play a part in adding another treasure-hunt to the golden glory of the world.

CHAPTER VI
NUGGETS!

Weeks had passed since the accident, and Jim was still in the hospital. The disaster had been costly to the colliery, but not crippling. The shafts — always the most costly portion of mine development — had not been injured. Many of the galleries had been reopened. The great ventilation fans were working again at full speed. The cages of coal were whirling up the shaft as of old.

Otto, after a short rest, had gone to work. The old miner was well satisfied with the fulfilment of his prophecies. The "knockers" had indeed tasted blood, for the two men in the old workings had never been found. As the mining engineer had supposed, that section of the mine must be abandoned forever. Moreover, Otto's forecast that Clem would be rescued, uninjured, also had come true.

Clem, indeed, was recovering, but the doctor declared him as yet unfit to resume the arduous work of hewing below ground. Accordingly, Owens had given him a temporary position as assistant to the safety inspector of the mine, for the accident had awakened the interest of the men in safety work, and the young fellow was quite competent to help in the simpler forms of instruction.

Anton was still in a weak state. His lungs were affected. He was living at home with his mother, Owens having granted the boy leave on full pay until he was entirely well again.

As the mine fell more and more into its old routine, Owens found himself oftener at the hospital. The remembrance of old times was strong in him, and the mine owner seemed to renew his youth in the rude speech of the prospector, sprinkled as it was with mining terms once so familiar to his ear.

Jim's liking for his employer was rapidly growing into comradeship. He was fully conscious of Owens' delicacy in never referring to the secret and began to feel that here, at last, was a rich man he could trust. In the course of time, it was the old prospector who brought the matter up, first.

"Has Clem ever said anything more to you about my mine?" he asked abruptly.

Owens started, but he got a grip on himself at once. When he answered, it was in as casual a tone as he could assume.

"Not another word. I don't suppose he has, to anybody. He seems to know enough not to talk. You heard how he snubbed the reporter!"

"I know. I heard him. He's square, is Clem. But I ain't never yet asked him what I said, down there in the mine. It's been eatin' me, all the time I've been lyin' here. To think I kep' it quiet all these years, an' then go blurt it out, jest 'cos I was hungry!"

"You haven't any reason to blame yourself for that, you were unconscious. And, like you, I believe Clem is as straight as a string."

"Ay," agreed Jim, "he shows color in every pan (specks of gold in every handful of washed sand). I'd ha' gone West, judgin' from what he said the other day, if it hadn't been for him."

"You certainly would."

"An' that makes us pards (partners) in a way, don't it?"

Jim paused, and then burst out again, "But I can't help wonderin' jest how much I told!"

"You'll have to ask Clem that. You remember, he said nothing to the reporter except that, in your delirium you were talking about gold."

"Gold! Did I say gold? Are you dead sure that I said gold?"

"That's what Clem told, anyway."

"Then I must sure ha' been dreamin'!" Jim's tone was both embarrassed and evasive.

Owens saw, at once, by the prospector's manner that he was nervously fearful of having betrayed himself and that he wanted to drop the subject. This seemed a sure sign that the hinted discovery was true.

It was a ticklish moment. The mine-owner realized that if the matter were dropped, now, he might never have another chance to get back to it. Any attempt on his part to renew the subject would be sure to arouse Jim's suspicion. If he were to be of any service to the old prospector, he must seize the present opportunity.

"Too bad that it isn't gold then," he said, half commiseratingly. "There's nothing in all the world that can make a man rich in a minute, as gold can. I saw that, often enough, in Australia. That's the land of nuggets, Jim, big ones! Most of them were found by sheer luck, and it was poor men who found them, too, mostly.

"The Australian black-fellows — pretty much savages, those fellows — knew gold, long before the white men came. They used to make their javelin-heads of gold because it's the easiest metal to work, when cold, and is found pure.

"So it was not so surprising, Jim, that one of the first big gold finds was made by a black-fellow, a husky tattooed chap who owned no property except a small apron of matting for his middle, a bunch of feathers for his hair, a long-handled stone hatchet, and a boomerang.

"This Cl'ck, as he was called, was employed as a shepherd by Dr. Kerr, a large sheep-owner in New South Wales. Cl'ck was a fairly intelligent fellow and had learned to talk a few words of English. He knew gold when he saw it. Just at the time I'm speaking of, the whole world was excited over gold, for it was just after the discovery of gold in California in 1848 and the great gold rush of '49."

"My father was one of the 'forty-niners,'" put in Jim, eagerly.

"So you're of the real Argonaut breed, then!" exclaimed Owens, but he did not push the enquiry, preferring to allow Jim to tell his story in his own way and in his own time. In order, however, to keep the subject of gold present in Jim's mind, he continued:

"For some time there had been vague hints that there might be gold in Australia, but, before the time of the 'forty-niners' no attention had been paid to it.

"For example! Once, in 1834, a ticket-of-leave man (convict out on parole), working in New South Wales, found a small nugget of pure gold in the earth and brought it to the nearest town to sell. Being a convict, he was at once arrested for having possession of the gold, and not being able to explain how he had got it. His story that he had found it in the earth was laughed at, for never — so far as the Australians knew, then — had gold been found in nuggets. As it happened, a white settler had lost a gold watch a little time before. The weight of the nugget was just about that of the weight of the case of a gold watch. The ticket-of-leave man was accused of having stolen the watch, thrown away the works and melted down the case. Hewas found guilty and punished with a hundred and thirty lashes."

"Whew, that was pilin' it on heavy!" commented Jim.

"They had to be severe in those days," Owens explained. "Botany Bay and Port Jackson were penal stations. In those days there were about fifty thousand white folks in New South Wales and three-quarters of them were convicts. That meant ruling with an iron hand, if mutiny was to be prevented.

"Twice, after that, white settlers found signs of gold, but in such small quantities that the deposits were not worth working by the primitive means employed at that time. In 1841, signs of gold were found not far from Sydney, the capital of New South Wales, but the Governor personally asked the finder to keep the matter a secret for there were 45,000 convicts in the colony by that time, and he was afraid that news of a gold-find might start a revolt that the military would not be able to quell.

"Two years later an even more curious discovery was made. Mr. H. Anderson, who owned a sheep-station where now are found the great gold-fields of Ballarat — in the province of Victoria, south of New South Wales — threw away the finest chance to become a multi-millionaire that ever came to any man.

"While walking from the home kraal (corral) to his house, in company with a neighbor, he saw on the ground a small piece of white quartz shining in the sun and noticed a few thin streaks of yellow in the quartz.

"He picked it up in a casual way, cast a glance at it, and handed it to his companion.

"'We're the richest men in the world,' he said, jokingly. 'You and I are running sheep over a gold-mine.'

"This jesting statement was literally true.

"But the other, who knew just enough about such matters to be really ignorant, wanted to display his small store of knowledge.

"'Gold!' he said contemptuously, 'that's what they call fool's gold. It's pyrites of some sort. Tut, tut, man! Golden nonsense! The only gold in this country is what grows on the backs of sheep.'

"Mr. Anderson, trusting to his companion's supposed better knowledge, threw the piece of quartz at a pair of wallabies (small kangaroos) that were leaping about, near by, and thus lost the chance of becoming the richest man in Australia. Five years later came the news of the gold-finds in California, and the more thoughtful men in New South Wales remembered these vague stories about gold having been found in the island continent.

"Now, let us get back to Cl'ck. His employer, Dr. Kerr, had bidden him keep his eyes open for any signs of gold, during his wanderings over the wild pasture land with his flocks. He promised to give him five pounds — a large sum for a black-fellow, in those days — for any piece of gold he should bring in, no matter how small.

"One day, in February, 1851, while leading his flocks to water at Meroo Creek, Cl'ck happened to see what looked like a smudge of yellow on the surface of a good-sized bowlder of quartz. He chipped at it with his long-handled hatchet, and there, solidly embedded in the bowlder, was a huge chunk of gold. It weighed over 102 pounds and was sold for over $20,000.

"This accidental discovery, which made Kerr rich, and which, incidentally, gave Cl'ck a hut and a sheep-kraal of his own, was amazing enough in itself. Even in California, which was then regarded as the very fountain-head of gold, no such nugget had been found. Yet, a couple of weeks later, a strike was made of such importance as to throw even the Black-fellow Nugget in the shade. This second strike determined the fortunes of Australia.

"One of the 'forty-niners,' who went to the California gold-fields in the first ship that sailed from Sydney after the news of the Sacramento discoveries had reached Australia, was a prospector called E. H. Hargraves. He got to California in the middle of the rush, but luck was against him.

"As happened so often with the men who knew only a little mining, he thought he could do better than merely follow the crowd. He staked a claim that looked more promising than the ground on the outskirts of the established mining camps. The claim proved worthless, or nearly so.

"Seeing the vast crowds streaming into California, and being convinced that there would not be gold enough for all, Hargraves decided to go home, rather than to stay in the California gold-diggings and die of hunger — as so many of the forty-niners did."

Jim nodded assentingly. He knew those stories. Many a one had his father told him. He was well aware that the trail of gold is a line of graves.

"On his way back home," Owens continued, "Hargraves remembered that he had seen ground in New South Wales which bore a marked resemblance to the regions where gold had been found in California. It was not ordinary alluvial gold land, such as prospectors were apt to seek, and no one had ever suspected that gold might be found there. Hargraves had kept his eyes open, when in California, and had realized that alluvial gold was but a beginning, that the biggest amount of wealth lay in a reef.

"Reaching Sydney in December, 1850, Hargraves made his way towards what is now the town of Bathurst. He was out in the field, prospecting, when the Black-fellow Nugget was found, and heard nothing about it.

"Near the end of February, 1851, working in Summerhill Creek, he discovered sure signs of gold, though in no such alluring quantity as had been found on the creeks leading into the Sacramento River. He worked steadily up the creek, not only panning as he went, but also striking off to right and left to see if the ground gave promise of a reef. There, on the last day of the month, he found a bowlder of quartz and gold, or, to speak more correctly, a detached piece of quartz from a reef, the greater part of which was almost pure gold and weighed 106 pounds.

"Hargraves was a man of sense. Instead of hurrying back to the nearest town with his find, selling it and blowing the money, he did some further prospecting. He collected specimens from different parts of the neighborhood, realizing that he had made a discovery not less sensational than when Sutter found the first gold in his mill-race in California.

"Then he went straight to the government authorities of New South Wales, and, in addition to establishing his own claims, he asked that a reward be given him by the government. The governor, anxious to stop the emigration from New South Wales to California, and realizing that a gold-find would bring enormous wealth and prosperity to the colony, made him a grant of $50,000 and a pension, providing that he would reveal the gold-bearing locality to the authorities, first, and providing the territory should produce a million dollars' worth of gold.

"Hargraves was as good as his word. He showed not only the famous Lewis Ponds, Summerhill, but also another and even bigger field on the upper waters of the Macquarie River. Owing to their prior information, the authorities were able to establish mining laws and good government before the rush set it, and Bathhurst was freed from the wild orgy of lawlessness which marked the days of the 'forty-niners.'

"All this, Jim, was a wonderful jump forward for New South Wales, and the town of Sydney boomed. But it was equally bad for the other provinces of Australia, and Victoria, being the nearest, suffered most. Almost every man able to wield a pick or rock a miner's cradle, deserted his work and rushed to Bathhurst. The gold was so easy to separate from the quartz that a man could get rich using no other tool than an ordinary hammer.

"Shepherds and even sheep-owners deserted their flocks, farmers let their land go to weed, merchants abandoned their shops, manufacturers allowed their machinery to rust, school-teachers locked the doors of schools, and workmen of every line of labor flocked to Sydney and toiled along the widely beaten track to Bathhurst.

"The authorities of the province of Victoria were in despair. The colony was plunging into ruin. Something must be done at once. They offered a huge reward to any one who should find gold within two hundred miles of

Melbourne. On the very same day, two men came to claim the reward. One had made a strike on the Plenty River, the other on the Yarra-Yarra. In August, 1851, came the discovery of gold at Ballarat, gold in its pure form and in large grains. The Bendigo fields developed immediately after.

"Then came a rush unparalleled! Money came easy, just as it comes easy to any man who has the good luck to be first at a strike. Every one got rich in Ballarat. There were no blanks. It was the richest ground that ever was found. The grains of gold were so big that they stuck out and looked at you!

"Geelong, which was the nearest town to Ballarat, was deserted. Three months after the discovery of gold the mayor of Geelong complained that there were only eleven men and over three thousand women and children in the town."

"Ay," agreed Jim, "and I remember in Pot-Luck Camp, the first time a decent woman came into the town, a miner offered her a bag of gold-dust to just shake hands with him. I've seen seven camps in a string, wi' maybe a thousand men in each an' nary a woman in the lot!"

"A camp like that becomes right wild," Owens agreed. "Ballarat, for a while, was about as dangerous a place as ever the world saw. Ticket-of-leave men from New South Wales, escaped or paroled convicts from Tasmania, roughs that had been run out of camps by vigilance committees in California, Chinese and Malays swarmed there. The diggers refused to take out licenses, fired on the police, charged the military stockade, and when the troops charged back and took 125 prisoners, a jury acquitted every one of the mutineers as upholders of individual liberty. If a man did not find gold, he starved at the exorbitant prices demanded for food; if he did make a strike, the chances were ten to one he would be murdered the next day. Colorado, at is worst, could not be compared with early days at Ballarat.

"Bendigo followed right after. That was a nugget corner. During the year 1852, alone, three big nuggets were found there, one of 24 pounds, one of 28 pounds, and one of 47 pounds. All these nuggets revealed outcrops and the finders all became rich men.

"One of them was found in a queer way. A prospector, or 'fossicker' as they call them back there, had been panning all along a small creek, finding hardly enough color to pay him for his day's work. He was walking on the very edge of the bank, scanning every stone he came to, but seeing no prospects. Suddenly the bank caved in under him, throwing him into the water. He came up, spluttering, and there, right in front of him, the water was washing off the dirt, was one of the purest nuggets that Australia ever produced. That was probably the most profitable bath in history."

"Some men are born lucky!" declared Jim, enviously.

"That's true," Owens agreed, "and it has been a characteristic of Australia that all the big finds have been made by lucky accidents. Even recent discoveries are no exception. Did you ever hear the story of Pilbarra and the crow?"

"Never did."

"It's a classic in Australian gold mining. It's as queer a story as I know. It doesn't sound true, a bit, but all the documents in the case are on record.

"One fine day, a youngster in West Australia — clear across the other side of the continent from Bathurst and Ballarat — was idling along a narrow track, as youngsters will, even when sent on a hurried message. On his way, he saw a black crow hopping some distance away. With a natural boy movement, he picked up a stone and shied it at the crow. The bird gave a loud croak and flew away a little distance, but in the same direction in which the boy was walking. Presently the crow was within throwing distance, again. The boy stooped to pick up another stone.

"Just as he was about to let fly, however, he noticed some gold specks in it and took it home. There he showed it to his father, who was an employe in the convict prison there. His father showed it to the Warden, as he was compelled to do, for he was also a convict, though a 'trusty.'

"The much-excited Warden knew that the governor of the colony ought to be notified at once, but how was he to do so without the secret leaking out through the telegraph office? Forgetting, in his excitement, that the governor did not know as much about the matter as he did, he sent the following message:

"'Boy here has just thrown stone at crow.'

"He entirely neglected to mention that there was anything special in either the stone or the crow.

"The telegram puzzled the governor not a little. But he had a sense of humor, and he replied to the Warden's telegram with the following message:

"'Yes; but what happened to the crow?'

"The Warden realized his former omission, and risking discovery, telegraphed:

"'Stone, gold.'

"The telegraph operator, not seeing how this could be a reply to the governor's question thought an error had been made and forwarded the message:

"'Stone cold.'

"The governor thought his friend the Warden must have gone crazy, but he was not to be outdone. He wired back:

"'Forward crow.'

"This time it was the turn of the Warden to be puzzled, and, as soon as his duties would permit, he went to the capital — almost a thousand-mile journey — taking, not the crow, but the stone filled with specks of gold. This was in 1888. Over half-a-million dollars' worth of gold was taken from Pilbarra before the end of the year.

"The richest gold field in Australia was hit on by accident four years later. This was Kimberley. Signs of gold had been found there in 1882, and again in 1886 but not enough to be worth working. In 1892 two prospectors started out to explore the region. They worked for weeks and found nothing. One of them, thoroughly disgusted, gave up the search and started for home.

"Two nights after, while camping, his horse became restless and started to plunge and kick at a wombat, near by. The prospector got up to quiet the beast, fearing he would break the picket-rope. On his way, he stumbled over a stone, which, in the light of early dawn, he saw to be rich in gold. He pegged out a claim at once, fetched his partner, and the two men took out $50,000 worth of gold in three weeks. This was the beginning of the great Coolgardie field.

"In the same region, about 24 miles away, not long after the opening of the Coolgardie field, a miner just missed wealth. There was a small camp there, but one man had no luck. While sitting dispiritedly in his dog-tent, just before going to sleep, he began to burrow with his fingers in the loose soil on which he was slouching and discovered a small pocket of gold. He was so excited that he shouted out the news to the camp.

"Before he could realize what was happening, the other miners crowded round, and pegged out claims to the very borders of his tent. All he got out of it was the small bit of ground on which his tent stood. The pocket only yielded a hundred dollars' worth of gold, his neighbors to right and left, got more than ten times that amount in the first three days.

"I could go on for hours, Jim, telling you about the Australian gold-fields, but I've said enough to show you that I meant what I said when I suggested that it was a pity that you hadn't found gold. The mining of every other metal needs a lot of capital to begin with — as gold does, when you begin to work a reef — but, in nearly every gold deposit, there are placers or pockets where a man can clean up quickly."

Jim's face was glowing with a lively interest. His excitement had grown as the mine-owner proceeded.

"And these here nuggets," he queried, "what makes 'em? Where do they come from? We don't find anything like that over here!"

"No," agreed Owens, "you don't. Chunks like 'The Welcome Stranger' which sold for $48,000 and which was found right in the road, the wheel of a passing wagon having cut through the soft earth and exposed it, are peculiar to Australia. Even South Africa, which is the largest gold-producing country in the world, hasn't any nuggets like that.

"As for where nuggets come from, Jim, that's a bit of a puzzle. Some say they grew in the earth, water heavily laden with gold, depositing more and more of the metal in the one place; other scientists claim that the nuggets were made in the days when the earth was all fire, and that the nuggets have been there ever since. Neither theory answers all the facts. It's truer to say that we don't know, yet, how nuggets came to be, nor why Australia has most of them.

"Some day, Jim, if you're interested, I'll try to explain to you the geology of gold. It's pretty complicated. I did a lot of study on it, when I was a young chap. Somehow, I seemed to be one of the men who didn't have any luck at the diggings. So I took to assay work (ore-testing), out there in Australia, and made more with my little assay outfit than most of the miners did with their claims."

Jim propped himself up on one elbow and stared fixedly at the mine-owner.

"You know how to make an assay, yourself?"

"Roughly, yes. Of course, only for field work, you understand. I don't pretend to be a mineralogical chemist."

"You can do it yet?"

"I suppose so. I haven't done any for years. This coal-mine business has kept me busy. But I've still got my portable assay outfit up at the house. I kept it for old-time's sake."

Jim's eyes glistened eagerly.

"You go to my cabin, Owens," he said, and it was noticeable that he dropped the "Mr.," "and five long paces due north from my kitchen window, you dig! You'll find a chunk of ore, there. Assay it, and then come back here!"

"But—"

The old prospector waved the interruption aside, impatiently.

"Do it, and then talk!"

Owens shrugged his shoulders and left, but little less excited than Jim.

That evening, during the middle of the night shift, when no one was likely to see him, the mine-owner went to the spot designated and began to dig. A foot or two beneath the surface, he found the chunk of ore. He put it in his pocket and hurried to his own house.

It was nearly dawn before he completed the assay. Then he put the ore and his memorandum of results in the safe and went to bed for a short sleep.

That morning, after breakfast, he returned to the hospital. He found Jim in an excited state.

"No, Mr. Owens, there's nothing wrong with him," the doctor explained, "only he hasn't slept all night. He's been asking for you, every few minutes."

When the mine-owner entered the ward, Jim struggled up to a sitting position.

"What about it?" he queried.

Owens closed the door carefully, came up to the sick man's bedside, and answered quietly,

"About 110 grains of gold to the ton and 800 ounces of silver. There's some native copper, too."

"It's a real find then?"

"It isn't what you'd call rich," the Australian answered cautiously.

"How about this, then?"

Jim took his old coat, which he had got the hospital attendant to bring him the night before, ripped open a seam, showing a narrow tube of buckskin running around the hem, and, opening its mouth, poured out a few grains of yellow metal into the palm of his hand.

"Free gold!" he said, triumphantly.

One glance of a trained eye sufficed.

"That's the stuff, sure enough. But you didn't find much of it, eh?"

"Where do you get that idea?"

"The grains are big enough to pan easily. If there was much of it, you wouldn't have left the place without cleaning up a good stake."

"There is plenty of it. But I had to get out."

"Why, then?"

"To save my skin. An' I couldn't get back there."

"Back where?"

"Where I found it."

"That doesn't tell me much."

"It ain't intended to."

"Then why," said Owens, showing irritation, "did you show me the ore at all?"

Jim looked at him under lowered eyelids.

"Have you ever been a prospector, honest?"

The owner of the coal mine put his hand in his breast pocket.

"I thought this might interest you," he said, "so I brought it along. That's me!"

He put his finger on one of the figures in the picture that he handed to the prospector. It showed a young fellow, bearded, in the typical Australian digger's rig-out, panning gold. The photograph was an old one, evidently, and there was no doubt that it was a resemblance of Owens in his youth.

"Ay, it's you," said Jim.

For some minutes there was silence. The mine-owner let the prospector think the matter out in his own way. Finally, with an air of desperate determination, Jim began:

"I'm gettin' old, now, an' times has changed since I found that ore. I ain't never give up hope of gettin' back there, but it don't look like it, now. I ain't the man I was. This last spell has crippled me up, pretty bad, too. I ain't never goin' to be right husky, again. The doctor says so."

"You can have a job above ground, here, as long as you want to."

Jim nodded appreciation of the offer.

"That's a square deal," he admitted. "But," he went on viciously, "I've had enough o' coal. I don't want to see a bit o' coal again, long's I live! I want to get back to God's country."

"Which is?"

"Where I found that!" replied Jim, evasively.

Owens made no protest. He kept silent, being sure that his companion would go on to talk.

"I'm gettin' old," Jim repeated, after a while, "an' it takes two things to get where I found that ore—a tough constitution an' money. I got neither. It's a job for a young fellow."

"I'm not much younger than you are," suggested Owens.

"Clem is."

"Well?"

"But he hasn't got any more money'n I have."

The mine-owner bent a level glance at the old prospector.

"Don't beat about the bush so much, Jim. If you don't want to say anything, why, drop the whole business. If you have anything to say, spit it out! You want me to grub-stake you? Is that it?"

"Me an' Clem. I won't do nothin' without Clem. A man has to have a pardner."

"I've no objection to Clem. On the contrary. But I don't grub-stake a man just because he shows me a bit of ore! I've been in the game too long for that. How do I know where that gold comes from? It might have been picked up from some mine now working at full blast. As for the gold-dust—why, it would be queer if you hadn't found some of it, somewhere.

94

"No," he went on, anticipating Jim's interruption, "I'm going to do the talking for a minute. You wanted to be sure I was a prospector. I showed you. You wanted to be sure I knew enough about gold to make an assay. I've done that for you.

"But confidence can't be all on the one side. You'll have to show your cards, the same way. You'll have to convince me that you're on the square, too. I'm not suspecting anything, mind, but this has got to be an open-and-shut deal, or I don't go in.

"Tell me who you are, where you've been, what you've done and what you know about gold deposits, anyway. I've got to know where you found this ore, how you came to find it, and why you haven't been able to get back there. You'll have to show me some proof, to start with, and what chances there are of taking the necessary machinery to the place, before I think about investing any capital.

"You can keep back the exact location of the strike to the last, if you like. If it sounds right, why, I'll think about it. But, mark you, Jim, I make no promises. You can talk, or not, just as you choose. I'm not hunting trouble, understand, this colliery keeps me busy enough. But if you want help, maybe I can give it to you. That ore deposit—if it's a deposit—can either be let alone or developed. If you let it alone, it's no good to anybody. If it's developed, there's a chance that it might make money for the both of us. Decide! It's up to you!"

Silence fell in the hospital ward. Jim's eyes were far away, evidently in that strange and distant land where he had made his find. Then he turned a piercing glance on the mine-owner, who returned it frankly.

The old prospector cleared his throat and swallowed hard. For a moment he seemed about to speak, and then stopped himself. At last his features settled into decision.

"Send for Clem to come here to-morrow," he said, "I'll tell the yarn."

CHAPTER VII

THE FORTY-NINERS

Several days elapsed before Jim took up his story, Owens preferring to wait until the prospector grew stronger. The mine-owner was shrewd enough to see that if he did not show too much haste, Jim would be less suspicious.

When the time arrived, Jim was up and dressed, though the doctor would only allow him out of doors for a few minutes at a time. The prospector had evidently been thinking out the beginning of his story, for, when his visitors arrived, he opened without preface.

"There's a lot o' wild yarns been told about the findin' o' gold in Californy," he began. "I've heard some, an' wild an' woolly they was; an' I've read some in books, an' they was wilder yet; an' I've seen some in the movies, an' they was a crime!

"Not but what them days wasn't tough! They was! The crowds what hit the minin' camps o' the Sierras in the fifties was out for gold an' nothin' else, an' they didn't much care how they got it. Father, he was a forty-niner himself, an' he was a rough un if anything got in his way. But he had more sense'n most, an', without any book-l'arnin' to speak of, he knew a heap about gold. If he'd been alive when I made my strike, old as he was, he'd ha' gone there, an' he'd ha' got there, too.

"I come o' Mormon stock, I do. My grand-pap, he made the trail to Salt Lake City wi' Brigham Young. Grandma, she used a rifle to defend the home camp, when the Illinois and Indiana folk came to massacre the women an' children, after the men were gone. Judgin' from what I've heard about her shootin', there wasn't many bullets wasted. Some o' these days, when you ain't got nothin' better to do, I'll tell you the story o' my grand-pap. He come to be one o' the Danites, later.

"You'll know the story o' Sutter's Mill, likely, Mr. Owens,"—Jim returned to the "Mr." in Clem's presence,—"but Clem, he don't know nothin' about it, an' he ought to be put wise if he's goin' to take a hand in this game.

"It all come about in queer fashion, a good deal like it did in Australia, as Mr. Owens was a-tellin' me a few days ago. The first signs o' gold was found on the Americanos River, which runs into the Sacramento. Found by accident, they was, too.

"There was a chap out them parts — an Indian-fighter — Cap'n Sutter by name. He owned a lot o' land an' used to run cattle in a small way, for the time I'm tellin' about was long afore the days o' the cowboys an' the ol' Texas-Drive trail. This Sutter had a foreman called James W. Marshall, who, besides his reg'lar job o' handlin' cattle an' greasers, looked after the runnin' of a one-horse saw-mill on the Americanos. It was an over-shot water-wheel mill, an' jest roughly chucked together.

"By-'n'-by Marshall begin to notice that the ol' mill wasn't workin' any too good. A lot o' sand an' gravel had come down wi' the water, chokin' up the tail-race some. The run-off wouldn't get away fast enough an' churned up under the water-wheel, causin' a loss o' power.

"To get the tail-race clear an' to widen her out a bit, Marshall, he throws the wheel out o' gear, pulls up the gate o' the dam, an' lets the whole head o' water in the mill-pond go a-flyin'. That water hit into the tail-race like a hydraulic jet an' scooped her out clear, carryin' a mass o' sand an' gravel into the river below.

"Next day, that was January 19, 1848, Marshall goes down to the river below the tail-race to see how she's shapin' an' if the cut-out is big enough. He's walkin' along the bank when he notices something glitter. He looks again, an' sees what he thinks is a bit o' Spanish opal, not the real gem, Clem, but a soft stone they find out there which looks even prettier'n an opal, but wears off an' gets dull in no time. They sell 'em to greenhorns, still.

"Marshall don't worry none about that, but by-'n-by, seein' a lot more, as he thinks, he figures to pick up some, jest to show. Accordin' as he used to tell the tale, he didn't think it was worth the trouble, but spottin' one that looks different from the rest, he reaches down into the water an' fishes it out.

"It ain't no opal at all. It's a bit o' shiny white quartz wi' a line o' yellow runnin' through. That's what makes the glitter. He hunts around some, rememberin' that he'd seen other bits shinin' yellow the same way, an' finds quite a few, all of 'em looking like scales o' pure gold. They was jest about the size an' thinness o' the scales that comes off a rattlesnake's skin after it's dry, an' for a while, Marshall figured they was some kind o' scale or horn, washed down thin by the water.

"In them times, the folks in Californy hadn't no idee o' minin'. It was still Spanish territory, for one thing, an', for another, there wasn't any minin' done. So Marshall wasn't thinkin' about gold. It was jest curiosity what made him hunt up some more o' those queer yellow scales.

"The more he found, the more puzzled he got. They was heavy; they bent like a bit o' metal, a thing a stone won't never do; they could be scratched with a pocket-knife; they didn't show no layers like horn does when it's old. The biggest bit he found weighed less'n a quarter of an ounce, an' this one was stickin' in the bank o' the tail-race, where the water had been washin' the earth away.

"He puts this last bit on a flat rock an' hammers it with a stone. It beats out flat quite easy. Marshall wasn't no fool, an' he knew there wasn't no yellow metal acted that way but gold or copper, an' native copper ain't that color.

"There was one o' the mill-hands wi' Marshall at the time, a chap called Peter Wimmer. He didn't know any more about gold'n Marshall did, but he'd heard said that every metal, savin' gold, gets black if it's boiled in strong lye. Marshall gets Wimmer to keep quiet by promisin' him a stake in whatever's found, an' tries the boilin' trick. The flakes o' metal stays put, an' shows nary a sign o' tarnishin'.

"By this time, Marshall was gettin' pretty sure that what he'd found was gold. He hadn't no notion of a gold mine, though, seein' he'd never heard of any. He reckoned that these flakes must be gold that had been buried by the Indians, long ago, an' had been washed down; from a grave, maybe, or some o' the treasure that the Spaniards had been huntin'.

"Jest the same, he was curious. He strolled away from the tail-race, idle-like, an' started huntin' promiscuous. He found specks o' gold all over. That settled him. He jumped on a horse an' rode down to Cap'n Sutter wi' the news.

"Sutter was a whole lot more excited than Marshall was. He was educated an' knew the history o' Mexico. He knew the Indians in Californy had possessed gold in the time o' the first comin' o' the Spaniards, an' he reckoned that gold must ha' come from somewhere. There'd always been some talk o' gold around where the Spanish missions had started, and, jest three years afore, a Spanish don had sent some ore to Mexico, sayin' that there was gold an' silver a-plenty around, an' the government had better get busy an' develop it. But the Spaniards weren't havin' any. Ever since they got so badly fooled, a couple o' hundred years afore, in their hunt for the 'Golden Cities o' Cibola,' they let Californy alone.

"Sutter didn't waste no time. He rode right back to the mill wi' the foreman. They didn't have to poke around long afore Sutter was plumb sure it was the real stuff. There was some of it in the Americanos, but the gold was even thicker in the dried-up creeks an' gulches that run into the river on both sides. With his penknife, Sutter pried out o' the rock-face a piece o' gold weighin' nigh two ounces.

"Some o' the mill-hands had got wise, too. Maybe Wimmer talked—though he said he hadn't. Maybe they just got a hunch, when they saw Sutter an' Marshall prospectin' around. They started huntin', too, but the flakes were small an' took a long time to find. None o' them knew enough to try washin' the sand, an' all they found didn't amount to much.

"Sutter took samples o' the gold to the fort at Monterey, where General Mason was in command. Mason was more interested in tryin' to keep the Apaches an' Comanches quiet than he was in fussin' about metals. He was a soldier, an' minin' wasn't his line. But he knew that the federal authorities at Washington ought to be notified.

"There weren't no post nor telegraph in them times—that was 'way afore the days o' the Pony Express, even—an' Mason sent a special messenger. Politics were queer in Californy around that time. Spain claimed the territory, the United States claimed it, an' for a while—a month, maybe—Californy was a republic on her own. The messenger reached Washington, all right, an' his report hurried up the signin' o' the treaty which made Californy American. That happened jest six weeks after Marshall had picked up his first bit o' gold an' only two weeks after the messenger arrived. Word was sent to Mason to be sure an' keep law an' order, no matter what happened. It was a bit too late, then; goin' an' comin' from Washington took months.

"Things were happenin' out 'Frisco way. Geo. Bennett, who'd been workin' at the mill, left there about the middle o' February, takin' some flakes o' gold with him. When he got to 'Frisco, he met Isaac Humphrey, who'd worked on the Dahlonega strike, in Georgia, in 1830. Humphrey took jest one look at the stuff, an' said right away that it was gold.

"Bennett an' Humphrey hot-footed it back to the mill. They found it workin' jest as usual. Some o' the men had picked up more gold, but casual-like, after workin' hours. Marshall hadn't done any more prospectin'. Sutter was waitin' to hear from Mason.

"Humphrey, bein' a gold miner, panned up an' down the river, an' found plenty o' color. He got quite excited an' declared it was richer'n the Dahlonega field, which had been pretty good, though the surface diggin's had petered out fast."

"What do you mean by 'he panned up and down the river and found color?'" queried Clem.

Jim gave a short laugh of surprise.

"That's right," he said, "you don't know nothin' about prospectin', do you? I'll tell you. Pannin' is how a prospector gets gold. It sounds easy, but there's a trick to it, jest the same.

"A prospector's pan is just like an ordinary tin wash-pan, wi' slopin' sides, only it's smaller; about a foot across at the bottom, an' made of iron, not tin. Many a hundred men have got to be millionaires with nothin' but a pick, a shovel, an' a pan.

"Supposing now, you're at the gold diggin's. You fill your pan, near full, with sand or with gravel or earth, or whatever stuff you think may have a little gold mixed up with it—"

"Can't you see the gold, then?" queried Clem.

"Not often, you can't. It don't lie around the ground like twenty-dollar gold-pieces! Some o' the richest placers ever found have the gold ground down so fine that it ain't much bigger'n grains o' dust.

"Well, havin' nigh filled the pan, like I said, you take it to the river, an' squattin' down, you hold it jest below the surface o' the water, one side a trifle higher 'n the other, so the water jest flows continual over the lower lip o' the pan. Then you give it a sort of rockin' an' whirlin' motion, so," — he illustrated with his hands, Owens smilingly doing the same, "lettin' the lighter mud flow out over the top.

"You keep on doin' that, without stoppin', for ten minutes or more. By the end o' that time, you're rockin' pretty hard, for the heavier stuff has got to be flicked out; but you've got to mind out, for if you go too hard, the gold — if there is any — will go out, too.

"Then you stop, pick out any pebbles in the bottom, lookin' at 'em hard — for they might show color — an' rock an' whirl the pan some more. If you've done it right, when you're through, there isn't more'n a handful o' sand an' grit at the bottom. You look at that as closely as you know how, an' if here an' there's a little speck o' yellow, you've found color. That's gold. You spread that handful out in the sun to dry an' blow away the lighter part. What's left is gold."

"Always supposing that there was some gold there to start with," put in Owens. "How many times have you panned, Jim, without finding any color?"

"Millions, I reckon! I panned every day an' all day, once, for two years, without gettin' enough gold dust to fill a pipe-bowl, an' then I got a double-handful in half a day. In general, you're doin' all right if you can get out of each pan enough dust to cover a finger-nail. So now you know what pannin' is, Clem."

"It's not such a cinch, at that!" the young fellow commented.

"But you may strike it rich any day, any hour, any minute!" Jim exclaimed, the fever of search in his eyes. "When Humphrey got up to Sutter's Mill, the first man to know anything about gold-washin' that got there, he was takin' out a thousand dollars a day, easy, for a month or more. The placers were rich."

"A 'placer,' Clem," Owens interrupted to explain, "is a deposit where there is gold mixed with sand, or gravel or mud. It is always a deposit which has been washed down by water, either a river which is actually running, or which is found in a dry bed where a river used to run. Mining people call it an 'alluvial or flood deposit.' Most of the gold-strikes have been found in this way. Go ahead, Jim."

"Right about the time that Humphrey was prospectin' an' doin' handsomely, an Indian, who had worked on placers in Lower California, told another o' the mill-hands how to get hold o' the dust. Besides that, a Kentuckian, who'd been spyin' on Marshall an' Sutter, had noticed that they'd found gold not only in the tail-race, but up the creeks. Both of 'em went down to 'Frisco.

"It was interestin', but nobody got excited. Gold strikes weren't known yet. There'd only been two gold rushes in the United States afore, neither of 'em big ones.

"The first was in North Carolina. A young chap, Conrad Reed, was shootin' fish with a bow and arrow in Meadow Creek. He saw in the water a good-sized stone with a yellow gleam. Pickin' it up, he found it heavy — seventeen pounds it weighed — an' he reckoned it was some kind o' metal, but he didn't think o' gold. That was in 1799. The stone was used to prop open a stable door for a couple o' years.

"One day, runnin' short o' groceries an' bein' shy o' ready cash, Reed thought he'd go into Fayetteville an' see if, maybe, he could raise a few dollars on the stone, as a curiosity. He took it to a jeweler, who said he thought there might be gold in it, an' told the young fellow to come back in the afternoon.

"When Reed came back, the jeweler showed him a thin wire o' gold, about as long as a lead pencil, an' said that was all the gold in the chunk. He offered Reed $3.50 for the gold an' Reed took it. How much the jeweler kept for himself, no one can't say.

"That started a little local talk, an' one or two men begun prospectin' in a shiftless sort o' way. They found nothin'. In 1813, some placers were found an' there was a mild rush, but it died right out. There was gold there, sure enough, but scattered so's a man didn't earn more'n a day's wages at washin'. Jest the same, all the gold in the United States came from North Carolina for twenty years after that, more'n a hundred thousand dollars' worth bein' sent to the Mint. But that's durn little, when you come to look at it, less'n fourteen dollars a day. An' that's not much for a bunch o' men!"

"No," admitted Owens, "you couldn't start a gold rush on that. And the second strike, Jim?"

"That was the Georgia deposits, at Dahlonega, where Humphrey came from. They're workin' yet, though small potatoes beside Californy an' Colorado.

"Californy was jest about uninhabited, then. There was only fifteen thousand folks in the whole durn State in 1848. Over a hundred thousand more came in the two years followin'. O' that lot, ninety per cent. was prospectors an' the rest was sharks, livin' off 'em. At the time o' the strike, 'Frisco didn't boast a hundred houses wi' white folks in them, an' they didn't know nothin' about Georgia an' Carolina gold.

"On May 8th, though, one o' the mill-hands come down from Sutter's Mill. He'd quit work to try gold-findin' on his own, an' takin' a tip from Humphrey, he'd washed out 23 ounces in four days. A 'Frisco man paid him $500 for his dust, cash down. That was good earnin's for four days.

"Sudden, the fever hit! The news got over the little town like a prairie fire durin' a dry spell. By night, half the town was talkin' gold; next mornin', the other half. Nine out o' every ten men quit work. A pick an' shovel an' a tin pan was worth a hundred dollars before night. One man paid a thousand dollars for an outfit, includin' a tent an' a month's grub. He was found dead half-way to the diggings, murdered for his outfit.

"The more excited ones an' those with the least money an' sense, started right off on foot, though it was all of a hundred an' fifty miles to Sutter's Mill, an' no trail, sixty o' these miles across a desert without water. No one ever did know how many o' that bunch ended up by feedin' the turkey buzzards.

"On the 14th an' 15th, a whole fleet o' launches an' small boats started out across San Francisco Sound an' Pablo Bay an' up the Sacramento River, every boat loaded to the gunwales. They said there was 2,000 men on the way.

"That wasn't jest a rush, it was a stampede. Not ten men in the entire crowd knew the first durn thing about prospectin'. They had some fool idee that pannin' gold was like pickin' flowers, all you had to do was to find it. Any one what knew better could ha' told 'em, but there wasn't any one to tell 'em, an' likely, they wouldn't ha' listened if he had. What's the use o' talkin' to a crazy man? An' a gold-rush is a bunch o' lunatics. I know! I've been that way myself, more'n once.

"Out Salt Lake City way, the winter had been bad. We Mormons had gone to Utah to avoid bein' citizens o' the United States, an' the government had took in Utah as soon as we made it worth takin'. My grand-pap an' my father were sore at that, an' they decided to start off with a party for Californy, which was still Spanish.

"Right around the 1st o' May, they reached the Sacramento River an' heard about gold bein' found. They took it as a sign that Providence was protectin' 'em, an' settled right down there to pan out the stream. Travelin', as the Mormons always did, with a proper leader, they pitched an organized camp. Trained to the last notch by their wanderin's in the wilderness, there wasn't a tenderfoot or an idle man in the bunch, an', workin' steadily, they begun to clean up pretty good.

"Jest a month later come the first wave o' the rush from 'Frisco. They struck the placers, their mouths fairly waterin' for gold, only to find the Mormons there already. That was a bit too much! After all their trouble an' misery, all the expense, all the deaths, they come to find all the claims along the strike staked out by Mormons.

"Durin' this time, Californy had been taken over by the United States. The 'Frisco bunch knew they'd be protected by law for anything they did against the Mormons, an', after a short pow-wow, they tried to rush the camp.

"But my grand-pap, an' some more o' the leaders, who were right handy with their rifles, were standin' at the ready. They'd fought their way across the plains, when the redskins were swarmin', an' they weren't the kind to take back water before a crowd o' tenderfeet. The 'Frisco men, city chaps a lot o' them, begun to waver, an' asked a parley.

"The Mormon leader, he told 'em, cold, what they'd get if they come any farther, an' hinted, pretty broad, that there was more cold lead around those diggin's than there was gold. But he told 'em, too, that there was a lot o' the other placers around wi' no one washin' 'em. The others grumbled but got out. Luckily, there was gold enough for all, at first. Later on, there was a sure-enough fight over a sluice, and the bullets went thick. The Mormons knew how to shoot, an' there was fifty o' the Gentiles dead when they broke back. Our folks were let alone on the Sacramento, after that.

"Durin' this month, John Bidwell struck it rich on the Feather River, 75 miles away from Sutter's Mill, and Pearson B. Reading on the Clear River, 100 miles further on. The news scattered the 'Frisco crowd, many a man leavin' a good claim in hopes to find a better. Others went prospectin' on their own. By the end o' the year, along the whole western slope o' the Sierra Nevada, from Pitt River to the Tuolumne, there wasn't a stream or a creek or a dry ravine that didn't have some one prospectin' or pannin' on it.

"Most o' those that got on to the diggin's in the first two months made money an' made it fast. A few struck bonanzas and took out a thousand dollars a day. Quite a lot got good pickin's an' cleaned up at the rate of a hundred a day. The rest were doin' good if they cleaned up twenty, an' that was jest about enough to live on, at minin'-camp prices. I've seen potatoes sell at five dollars apiece to be eaten raw, when the scurvy was ragin', an' three men were killed in a fight over the buyin' of a fresh cabbage.

"Those was tough times, even for the first lot that come from 'Frisco. There was no sort o' law an' order in the camps, no sanitation an' no doctors. Typhoid an' dysentery got a good hold by the end o' June. You could get the reek o' fever an' disease a mile away.

"Men too sick to walk crawled out to their claims an' died there, scary lest some claim-jumper should seize their claims. Hope stuck with 'em to the last. Scores fell dead into the stream, wi' the pan still in their hands. One time, when they come to carry a dead man from beside his pan, that he hadn't time to clean up afore death took him, there was the first color in it that had been found on the claim. It brought in a pile o' money later.

"Later, when the real forty-niners came, men o' red blood, vigilance committees were organized an' the camps got sort o' human. But at the start, it was ugly. If a man didn't clean up quick, he starved. If he did, somebody jumped his claim, or put a bullet in him. If the body of a miner was found floatin', it was called accidental death, even if his head was blown off, for, the sayin' used to go, 'A miner ought to carry enough gold dust on him to sink.' Scores, aye, hundreds, died o' gun-play.

"About the fine breed o' men that come later, the forty-niners that crossed the whole plains o' the West from Missouri to Santa Fé an' beyond, men that brought their women an' children in long lines o' prairie schooners, keepin' scouts out ahead an' one each side, fightin' famine, thirst an' redskins all the way, you won't want me to tell you. Every American knows their story.

"But every one don't know what them trains o' gold-seekers looked like, when they reached the diggin's! My father's told me, though.

"He's seen 'em reach the Sacramento, half-scalped an' with wounds that never healed. He's seen swingin' at their saddles the scalp-locks o' Indians they'd scalped theirselves. He's seen women come in with nary one o' their men-folk left alive. He seen 'em come in crazy, never to be sane again, after the horrors o' that trail. He's seen a man come in safe an' untouched, after wheelin' a wheelbarrow nigh three thousand miles. He's seen seven men an' nine women get to the Sierras out of a party of 118, leaving 102 dead on the road.

"I've heard tell, an' I believe it, that across the desert stretch a man could ha' walked for forty miles an' put his foot on a bone at every step. An' o' those who did reach, most o' them were so weak that camp fever an' dysentery took 'em off like flies. A good half died at the diggin's before they ever found a bit o' gold.

"How many o' the forty-niners died at sea? There's no tellin'. Ships set out from all corners o' the globe. There was a wild rush from England. That meant goin' round the Horn, an' there weren't many steamships, then. Sailin'-ships, so rotten that their owners were glad to get rid of 'em, were sold to forty-niners at fancy prices. In one week, eighteen ships sailed from England to go round the Horn to Californy an' seven arrived. The gold o' Sutter's Mill called many a good man to leave his bones on the ocean bottom.

"But it wasn't all bad luck an' dyin'. Lots o' the diggers struck it rich an' spent it quick. Gamblin' an' drinkin' an' work—that's all there was to a minin' camp in them days. Spendin' freely give a man a minute's glory. Treatin' the crowd was the only way to be popular. An', in a minin' camp, where there's no women to live with, no children to think of, no homes to go to, what is there but the saloon, an' what's the use o' the saloon without friends! A bag o' gold-dust was enough for a spree.

"Gold-diggin' don't go to make a man careful. It's always to-morrow that's goin' to be the lucky day. What's the use o' savin' ten dollars when a stroke o' the pick or a swirl o' the pan may suddenly give a man a thousand? So they thought. One miner found a pocket that netted him $60,000 in two weeks, an' when he sobered up, he hadn't six dollars' worth o' dust left.

"There was some that stuck to their earnin's, just the same, but they was either quick with a gun or slow wi' their tongues. Six brothers come out from England, none o' them ever havin' roughed it before, but they stuck together an' stayed sober. They were let alone, because to touch one meant to fight six. They went back to England, at the end o' the first season, with a million dollars between 'em.

"One man, who started out from 'Frisco wi' a drove of a hundred hogs, figurin' on sellin' 'em in the minin' camps for fresh meat, reached Feather River wi' five. But he sold those five for more'n twice as much as he'd paid for the hundred. An' that was only the beginnin'! On the way, his hogs rootin' in the ground had uncovered two pockets. He covered the places an' marked 'em wi' crosses, so's folks should think they was graves. On his way back, he took $5,000 out o' one pocket an' $10,000 out o' the other. An' then some folks try to make out that there ain't no such thing as luck!"

"But is it all so chancy as that?" queried Clem. "Surely if a chap knew in what sort of ground or near what sort of rock gold was generally found, he'd have some idea where to look."

"Sure he would," agreed Jim, "but gold goes where it durn pleases, an' that's the only rule I know. O' course, every prospector has his own idees, same as he has for playin' poker, but he don't win any quicker because o' that. Leastways, not so far as I've seen.

"As for judgin' by the rock an' the color o' the soil, why, you can take your pick. Take San Diego County, Californy, where I've worked, the gold lies in schist, sometimes blue, green, or grey. In the Homestake, South Dakota, red looks good, a sort o' rotten quartz stained with iron. Black flint's a good sign in Colorado. Snow-white quartz is often lucky. Purple porphyry sometimes has veins that work up rich. An' I've seen gold come out o' pink sandstone, yellow sandstone, all shades o' granite, an' even coal!"

Clem turned an incredulous glance at Owens, but the mine-owner nodded agreement.

"Jim's right," he said, "color isn't any clue. Gold can be found in any kind of rock. So far as that goes, it shows up in strata of any geological age. There's gold everywhere. There isn't a range of hills in any country of the world which may not contain gold. There isn't a bed of sand or gravel that may not be auriferous. Even the sea beach, in places, has yielded fortunes. For that matter, there's gold in every bucket of water you dip up from the sea.

"But there's not much of it. Geologists have figured that there's about one cent's worth of gold to every ton of rock in the earth's crust, but it would take fourteen dollars a ton to handle it. There's about a hundredth of a cent's worth of gold in a ton of sea water, and it would cost about ten dollars a ton to get it out. Not much chance of getting rich that way, is there?"

"I should say not," declared Clem, with decision.

"But, as Jim has been pointing out, gold isn't scattered evenly all through the earth. In some places, it's moderately plentiful, in others it's scarce or entirely absent. Prospecting for gold, Clem, doesn't mean looking for a place where there is gold, but looking for a place where the proportion of gold to the soil or to the rock is high enough to give a profit in the working of it.

"It isn't always the place where the gold is most plentiful that gives the greatest profit, either. A low-grade ore, that is a rock containing only a small proportion of gold, may be worth a great deal if it is near the surface, if the rock is easily crushed, if it is near water-power, and if transportation is not too difficult.

"A high-grade ore, in which there is a large proportion of gold, may be worth a good deal less, if it is more difficult to work and less easy of access. The richest gold-field in the world, that of the Rand, in South Africa, which gives one-third of the total gold output of the world, is of an ore so poor that a forty-niner would have turned up his nose at it, and the machinery, even of thirty years ago, could have done nothing with it. Nearly all the big mines of to-day are winning wealth out of low-grade ore.

"Some of these days, Clem, I'll explain the geology of gold to you, and show you how it is that the mines which give the richest specimens are sometimes the poorest mines to work. But I'm breaking into Jim's story."

"I was jest a-sayin'," continued Jim, who had listened with impatience to Owens' explanation, "that them as says there ain't no luck in minin' ain't never done no minin'. I've been showin' you how some men got rich in a minute an' hundreds got nothin'.

"But there was some fields that was a frost, right from the start. They promised big an' give big for the first scratch or two. Then — nothin'! Kern River was one o' those an' Father got bit.

"My grand-pap, he'd gone back to Utah to take command of a band o' 'Destroyin' Angels', as the Gentiles called the Danites, leavin' Father to go on pannin' on the Sacramento. The claims was peterin' out fast, but there was good day's wages to be got, still.

"Then, in 1855, come the news o' the Kern River strike. If folk had gone crazy in forty-nine, they got crazier still this time. There was all the fame o' the last strike to lure 'em on. The same ol' story o' desert trails without water, o' minin' camps that were death-traps, was repeated, only ten times worse. Twenty thousand started in the same week. The last few miles was a trail o' blood. Men stabbed their friends in the back to get to the diggin's first. The stakin' o' claims was done, six-shooter in hand.

"And, o' the twenty thousand, there wasn't twenty that cleaned up rich. My father, he wasn't one o' the twenty. He prospected, up an' down, until he'd spent the last ounce o' gold-dust he'd got from five years' work, an' all but starved to death on his way across the desert, headin' for Utah.

"When he got into Nevada, he didn't have a pound o' flour left. He didn't have nothin' left, nothin' but his pick an' shovel an' pan. All the rest was gone. He didn't have no trade but prospectin'. Well enough he knew he'd leave his bones on the trail if he tried to foot it to Salt Lake City.

"He'd heard about gold being found on the Carson River, in Nevada, in 1850, by Prouse Kelly and John Orr, an' he knew that they'd gone back an' done well. Several other small placers had been found, noways rich, but still enough to keep a busy man goin'. He'd learned from his Kern River experience that a man did better, stickin' to a small claim'n tryin' for the big prizes, an' he made for the small placers o' the Carson River. A store-keeper grub-staked him, to start with, an' in a month or two, he was clear.

"Next year, that was '56, his pard struck what looked like a silver vein, an' started off to the city wi' some samples. Father, he stuck by the gold. That's where he lost out. He prospected in Six Mile Cañon an' found little color — his bad luck again, for, in '57, two prospectors made a rich strike less'n a quarter of a mile away from where he'd been pannin'. They found signs o' silver, too, but chucked the stuff aside. Father plugged along, an' at last struck a little pocket in a creek off the Carson. A month's work gave him near a thousand dollars' worth o' dust, an' he reckoned he'd go back to Salt Lake City. He'd been away eight years.

"Grand-pap was still alive an' told Father to stay home an' go farmin'. But it didn't go. The prospectin' bug had hit Father too hard. In the spring o' '59 he started back for the Carson River again, an' Mother come along. She reckoned she might never see him again, if she didn't.

"That summer, there was three folks on the claim. Another pard had come, a little one, what had for his first toy a nugget o' gold tied on a bit o' string. I was born on a minin' claim, for that little pard was — me!"

CHAPTER VIII
THE GREAT BONANZA

"You certainly started young enough in the prospecting game," said Owens, when Jim told of his birth in a mining camp, "and have you been at it all your life?"

"Ever since I was big enough to twirl a pan or rock a cradle!"

"How do you mean rock a cradle?" queried Clem. "I thought you were in the cradle!"

"Not that kind, boy," Jim answered, "what I'm meanin' is a miner's cradle, or a rocker, as some calls it. I gradooated from one to t'other."

"What's a miner's cradle, then?"

"It's a scheme to make pannin' easier. Pannin' is durn hard work, Clem. You're squattin' on your hams beside a river all the day long, you got to hold a pan full o' earth an' water at arm's length an' down at an angle what nigh tears your arms out o' their sockets, an' then keep revolvin' the mixture with a circular twist that wrenches the muscles somethin' cruel. I've seen big men, tough uns, too, fair cryin' from the pain, at first.

"Not only that, but you got to work the sodden lumps o' dirt soft wi' your fingers, so's the grit gets right into the skin. Your hands are wet nigh all the time. The grit an' the constant washin' o' the water, in all weathers, cracks the skin all over, so's it's bleedin' most o' the time. You got to have hands like a bit o' rawhide to stand it.

"The cradle does the work quicker'n' easier, but it takes three men to work it right. It looks like a child's cradle from the outside, though most o' them I've seen was made pretty rough. About six inches from the top there's a drawer, or sometimes jest a tray, with a bottom o' iron, punched wi' holes o' different sizes, accordin' to the kind o' dirt you're workin' in. If your pannin' out don't show no big grains o' gold-dust, why, you keep the holes o' the cradle small, otherwise, you got to have 'em bigger. Below that drawer is another one, slopin' like. It hasn't got no holes. It has cross-bars or cleats, what we call 'riffles,' to keep the gold from washin' away.

"One man digs up the pay dirt an' chucks it in at the top o' the cradle. Another dips up bucket after bucket o' water, continuous, an' sloshes it in; it's his job, too, to break up the soft lumps an' keep stirrin' the pasty mess, an' to keep the cradle full o' water. The third man goes rock, rockin', without stoppin', hours at a time. Mostly, the pardners spell each other off."

"But I should think a good deal of gold would be washed away by that system," objected Clem, "surely the rocking must dash some of it over the riffles."

"Some does go," Jim agreed, "but a gang can handle so much more pay dirt in a day that it more'n makes up. Three men with a cradle can handle twice as much dirt as the three men workin' separately would, each with a pan. Team work pays, in minin'—if you can trust your pardners.

"Just about the time I was born, Father made pardners with five other prospectors, all pannin' on the Carson. Their claims were all in a string, one after the other, so they figures on makin' a sluice. That's jest a long trough. In richer an' more settled camps they're made of iron, length after length, all ready to be fixed together like a stove-pipe, but on the Carson, they was jest hollowed-out logs.

"Sluices was always a foot deep, a foot an' a half wide, an' as long as could be made, slopin' slightly, so the water wouldn't run too fast or too slow, an' wi' riffles every few inches all along. The six claims I'm tellin' about give a chance for a sluice over a hundred foot long. To save the trouble o' liftin' water up in a pail, or pumpin' it, Father made a sort o' small flume, leadin' from the river higher up right into the sluice, so's the water would run continuous.

"Bein' there was six o' them, the pardners worked three shifts, eight hours each. One man dug the dirt, wheeled it in a barrow to the head o' the sluice an' dumped it on a wooden platform. The other shoveled it into the sluice, stirred it up, an' broke up the lumps when they got pasty. Eight hours o' that was a day's work, I'm tellin'! Mother, she cooked an' washed for all six men, aside lookin' after me. Wi' meals to be got for all three shifts, she was kep' busy.

"The sluice didn't stop runnin', day nor night, for a month at a stretch. Then the water in the flume was turned off, the sluice, riffles an' platform were scraped clean wi' knives, an' all six pardners panned the scrapin's. That was the clean-up. It was divided by weight o' dust into seven equal parts, Mother gettin' a man's share."

"Didn't they use any mercury at all on the Carson?" queried Owens.

"After a bit, our gang did. Not until each man had a bag o' dust set aside, big enough to buy a few weeks' grub, though. They'd all got badly bit in Californy, an' quicksilver cost a lot o' money in them days."

"What's the quicksilver for?" queried Clem.

"To catch the gold. If you spread it on the riffles it seems to grab a hold o' 'color' like glue, an', what's more, nothin' but gold'll stick to it."

"Why is that?"

"I don't know," Jim answered, a bit irritably, "it does, that's all."

Owens interposed.

"You can't blame Jim for not knowing why, Clem," he said. "So far as that goes, I don't believe any chemist in the world can tell you exactly why quicksilver catches gold. It does, though, sure enough. But I can show you how it does it, in a way.

"You know that if iron is exposed to damp air, it turns red with rust? That is due to the chumminess or the affinity of iron with oxygen. You know if silver is exposed to city air, where the burning of coal in furnaces and fireplaces sends a sulphurous smoke into the air, it turns black? That's due to the fact that silver is a natural chum of sulphur. Chemically speaking, they make compounds easily.

"It's the same way with mercury, or, as it is generally called, quicksilver. Gold and quicksilver are chums, and the minute they get together they join to form a mixture which is called an amalgam. That's one of the great discoveries of the age. Gold-mining has taken a big jump forward since that was found out.

114

"You can see yourself how that would work. Whether with a pan, a cradle, or a sluice, the only thing that enables a miner to separate the gold from the worthless dirt is that the gold is smaller and heavier. But suppose the gold dust is so fine as to be invisible, it will be so light as to wash away easily; if it is in fine flakes, the flakes will almost float. All that light gold would be lost in the dirt that flows out of the bottom of the sluice, the tailings, as they are called.

"In the days that Jim is describing, two-thirds of the gold was lost that way. Every one, absolutely every single one of the forty-niners would have made a fortune, if the chemistry of gold had been as far advanced then as it is to-day. Even now, men are working over with profit the tailings that the forty-niners threw away.

"Suppose, now, you make your sluice, cover the bottom of it and the riffles with copper plates to hold the quicksilver better, and then cover your copper with quicksilver. What happens when the dirt and water come flowing down the sluice? The riffles will catch your heavy gold, just as well as before, and the quicksilver will catch a lot of the light gold that used to escape. You've got your gold in the riffles, then, and you've got a mixture of gold and quicksilver which has formed an amalgam.

"Now, the mixture has to be made to give back that gold. First of all it is pressed through canvas or buckskin in order to get rid of the liquid quicksilver, which will pass through the weave of the first and the pores of the second, leaving inside only such of it as has firmly allied itself with the gold to form the amalgam.

"The next thing to do is to put this amalgam into a retort, out of which leads a long pipe, and to subject this retort to intense heat. Quicksilver is vaporized at a comparatively low temperature — for a metal. It is driven from the amalgam in the form of vapor, much as water may be driven off in steam. The quicksilver vapor passes along this long pipe, which leads to several coils placed in a tank of running cold water. The cold chills the vapor, condensing it into the liquid state again, and the quicksilver runs out of the end of the pipe, ready for use once more. The pure gold is left.

"But, even with the use of quicksilver on the sluice there was still 40 per cent. of the gold that got away. For many years there was no practical way of recovering this loss, and the chemists of the world tore their hair in despair. What was needed was to find some other chum of gold, even more affectionate than mercury. The chemists found this new friend, at last, in cyanide, which is a salt of prussic acid. Cyanide, Clem, is an arrant flirt, as I'll show you, in a minute.

"Nowadays, the tailings, after passing over the long sluice or flume, and after having dropped the heavy gold in the riffles and given some of the light gold to the quicksilver, are led to a huge churn. There the earth and water are pounded together into a sort of slime. A wheel lifts this slime into a movable chute from which it is poured into a series of vats or tanks. These tanks contain cyanide, which has already allied itself with a chum — potassium.

"But cyanide likes gold even better than it does potassium, and, as soon as the slime strikes the vat, the cyanide lets go the potassium and clings to the gold. Cyanide of gold is formed. So far, so good. But what the miner wants is pure gold.

"The cyanide is pumped up out of those tanks into another chute, which pours it into a second lot of tanks, fastened to the side of which are large bundles of zinc shavings. The cyanide liked the gold better than the potassium, but it has the bad taste to prefer zinc even to gold. It releases the gold and flies to the embrace of the zinc. The gold, suddenly deserted of the friendship of the cyanide, powders down to the bottom of the tank, in absolutely pure form, ready to be melted down into bars. By other processes, which I won't bother you by describing now, the zinc is released from the cyanide, and the cyanide is led to its old friend the potassium, ready to begin work anew. So, you see, nothing is wasted.

"This process, and this only, has made the astounding wealth of South Africa, for, as I told you, the reefs there are of very low-grade ore, so low that Jim, here, would have turned up his nose at it. The modern ability of chemists to get out the tiniest particle of gold that lies in the most stubborn rock has made the Rand a richer region than a prospector's wildest dream."

"If I'd known all that, forty years ago, I'd be a rich man now," said Jim, regretfully.

"You'd have been a millionaire, ten times over," Owens agreed, "but, since it hadn't been found out, you couldn't have known it. But did you always stick to gold, Jim? That Carson River country has got more silver in it than it has gold."

"Don't I know it? 'Ain't it been rubbed into me, good an' hard? Father wasn't a cussin' man, noways, but he couldn't keep his tongue in order like a man should, when he got to talkin' about silver. He threw away any amount o' high-grade silver ore, while huntin' for gold. The richest silver mine in the whole world, I reckon, was found less'n a hundred yards from where he'd been pannin'.

"It was the same ol' story—he didn't know enough! Workin' hard may bring a man some money, but havin' savvy will bring him a lot more.

"Right where Father was workin', he was havin' all sorts o' trouble wi' a heavy black sand that kep' on fillin' up the riffles like it was gold. He shoveled away cubic yards of it! An' do you know what that was? That dirty black sand was nigh pure silver, an' Father was pannin' less'n quarter of a mile away from the richest section in all Nevada. He was campin' right on the Comstock Lode! I reckon you've heard o' that, Mr. Owens!"

"Every mining man has heard of the Comstock," the mine-owner replied. "Personally, I don't know a great deal about silver, although the Broken Hill mine, New South Wales, which is nearly as rich as the great Nevada deposit, is located not far from my home. I went straight from gold to coal. So I never did hear the real story of the Comstock. But you ought to know about it, Jim. Was it found by accident, too?"

"Rank good luck an' rotten bad luck mixed," Jim answered. "Do I know that story! The first week's pay I ever drew was on the Comstock. An' I was born, as I told you, near enough to throw a stone right on to the Comstock outcrop. This was how it begun!

"There was two prospectors, Patrick McLaughlin an' Peter O'Riley, Irishmen both, what had been pannin' gold on Gold Cañon, where, I told you, Father had been. Luck was poor. Grub was hard to get. The water o' the Carson had a strong taste, an' wasn't none too healthy. So the two pardners started diggin' a water-hole down in the gulch, near where they was workin'. What come up out o' the hole was a yellow sand, all mixed up with bits o' quartz an' a crumblin' black rock, much the same as the black sand Father'd been worried with.

"Now a prospector'll wash any durn dirt he sees, an' O'Riley, while waitin' for some bacon to fry, chucked some o' the yellow an' black sand in a pan an' give it a twirl or two. You can reckon he jumped some when the pan showed color. He yelled to McLaughlin an' the two o' them got busy. Every pan showed color, not big, but enough. The cleanin' up wasn't what you'd call rich but it was steady, an' there was any amount o' pay dirt in sight. The two begin to fill their buckskin bags wi' dust, right smartly.

"Then a low-down, dirty, ornery coyote of a man, Henry Comstock by name, come amblin' along. A shifty critter was Comstock, trapper, fur-trader, gambler, claim-jumper, mine-salter, sneak-thief, an' everything else. He see O'Riley an' McLaughlin cleanin' up the cradle an' guessed they'd struck it rich. Lyin' glibly, like the yaller dog he was, he told the prospectors he was the owner o' the land, an' made 'em give up their claims. They went on workin', but on small shares. The hole got deeper, but by-'n-by got hard to work because this seam o' black rock got wider'n wider as it went down. Riley an' McLaughlin dodged the rock, the best they knew how, findin' gold enough to pay for workin' in the loose dirt on either side.

"One or two other prospectors drifted up that way, though the pickin's was small. One o' them, wonderin' what the black rock might be, an' havin' a hunch it might be lead it was so heavy, put a chunk in the hands of an assayer in Placerville.

"The expert couldn't believe his eyes, at first, an' thought some one was playin' a joke on him. His assay showed a value o' $3,000 per ton in silver an' $800 per ton in gold. He assayed one or two other bits, wi' the same result. Here was millions, jest beggin' to be picked up! Folks got wind of it, right away. That was in November, 1859, too late in the winter to cross the high Sierras into Nevada.

"The rush started a-hummin', early in 1860. 'Frisco was fair frothin' at the mouth. It was a long trail, an' the silver-hungry crowd couldn't wait. Some o' the craziest got away as early as January. They caught it heavy!

"From Sacramento up the old emigrant trail to Placerville weren't no gentle stroll in winter time! From Placerville to the bottom o' Johnson Pass was a trail for timber wolves, not for humans. Snow lay thick. Winds, fit to freeze a b'ar, come a-howlin' down the high Sierras. A few men got through an' froze to death on Mount Davidson, the silver actooally ticklin' the soles o' their feet. Some got caught in slow-slides in the Johnson Pass an' their bodies didn't show up till June. A lot more died o' starvation an' exposure on the way.

"That didn't keep the rest from comin'. They fair stormed the Pass. In March there was a thaw, an' the flood o' men broke through.

"It was a bad crowd. Aside from decent prospectors and miners, there was a pack o' gamblers, saloon-keepers, 'bad men,' fake speculators, an' all the rest o' the human buzzards that follow on the heels of a rush. They remembered the first days o' the forty-niners, an' every bad egg in Californy wanted to be the first to murder an' to rob. In three weeks, the silent an' deserted slopes o' Mount Davidson was peppered wi' tents. Virginia City had been started an' had become a roarin' town.

"That wasn't a minin' camp, it was a hell-hole. I've seen tough joints in my day, but Virginia City beat all. It wasn't jest the miners lost their heads, but experts, geologists, an' all, went plumb crazy. 'Twasn't much wonder. That black rock was jest one continooal bonanza. A gold mine was a fool to it.

"The ore in one of the shafts—the Potosi Chimney, it was called—was rangin' steadily over a hundred dollars a ton silver, an' that shaft alone was bringin' up 650 tons a day. Three prospectors tapped the big lode at another point, near Esmeralda, worked a week an' took six thousand dollars apiece for their claims. The man who bought first rights on Esmeralda, sold them before the end or that summer, for a quarter of a million. An' yet McLaughlin an' O'Riley havin' given up their claims to Comstock, got nothin' out of it. As for Comstock, he filed a false claim of ownership which the courts wouldn' give him, an' he went down an' out.

"The Gould & Curry mine, one o' the richest, was bought from its finders for an old horse, a bottle o' lightnin'-rod whisky, three blankets, an' two thousand dollars in cash. After four millions had been taken out of it, an Eastern syndicate come along an' bought it for seven millions o' dollars — an' they made money out of it, at that! Six years after the openin' o' the Gould & Curry, there was 57 miles o' tunnels, all in rich ore, an' the owners had to work it like a coal mine, leavin' great pillars o' silver to prop up the roof!

"A telegraph line was run through an' that made Virginia City ten times worse. It weren't a town o' miners, rightly, not like a gold placer camp. Silver ore needs capital to work it, an' Virginia City become a town o' loose fish, speculators, crooked brokers, an' suckers. One man sold the Eureka mine to eight different people at the same time, an' he'd never even seen the place an' didn't own a claim in it. He pocketed eighty thousand dollars in eight days an' was strung up to the limb of a pine-tree the ninth!

"There was some good work done, though. Durin' 1861 an' 1862 road-makers was busy, though laborers was gettin' fancy prices. But the engineers kep' at it, an' afore the winter o' '62, there was a wide road where two eight-mule coaches could cross each other at full gallop without slacking the traces. Tolls were high, so high that the road-makers got all their money back in the first year. Crack coaches with relays made the trail from Sacramento to Virginia City in twelve hours, instead of six weeks, like it was first. Hold-ups were frequent an' plenty, but a 'road agent' didn't last long where every one carried a gun.

"Then come the 'year o' nabobs,' that was '63. The Comstock Lode put out over $26,000,000 in silver bullion alone, half-a-million dollars o' silver every week in the year. By that time there was forty big minin' plants operatin' wi' steam machinery. There weren't no place for a small man any more, unless he wanted to do minin' on days' wages, an' mighty few o' the early prospectors ever got any o' the later wealth o' the Comstock. Father, he wouldn't touch silver, nohow, but he made more'n the miners did by pannin' the dirt the mines were throwin' away. They were makin' so much money out o' silver that they wouldn't bother to take out the gold.

"Then come the first big smash. Half o' the mines sold to the suckers weren't worth shucks. Wild-cat mines, they called 'em. There was one, the Little Monte Cristo, which give the promoter half a million dollars in shares which he sold to folk in New York an' Philadelphy. An' they never made more'n an 8-foot pit in it an' didn't take out enough bullion to melt down into a silver spoon!

"What was worse, the big mines got down to the rock water-level. At first, they run little tunnels, what they called 'adits' from the side o' the mountain an' drained that way. That wasn't no good, much. They soon got below that. The lode got richer the farther down they went an' some o' the big companies took to pumpin' out the water. Right away, they started in to lose money. It cost more to pump than the silver was worth. The boom dropped with a thud.

"Then Adolph Sutro come along. He was a big man was Sutro, one o' these here engineers folks talk about. He offered to build a drainage tunnel from the foot-hills o' the Carson Valley, just above the river smack into the heart o' the lode, a distance o' four miles, tappin' all the mines. He figured that, if it weren't done, all the mines'd get flooded an' all the wealth o' Comstock'd go to smash.

"Seein' things were going' so bad, the mine-owners balked at first. After a while, though, the water come in so free that they all agreed to give him two dollars a ton for all the ore raised from the mines, providin' his tunnel drained 'em all, an' providin' he fixed it so that they could get men an' material through the tunnel, instead o' having to pull it all up the shaft. It took Sutro six years to get the capital, but he got it. He begun work in '71. Toward the end o' the job the work was so hot an' tough that he doubled his rate o' wages, an' in '77, bein' eighteen years old then, I started operatin' a drill in the tunnel. I was thar on the day that we broke through."

Few engineering feats in the history of mining are more famous than the making of the Sutro Tunnel. In one of the publications of the U. S.

Geological Survey, Eliot Lord has told its story of perseverance and triumph.

"Sutro's untiring zeal," wrote Lord, "kindled a like spirit in his co-workers. Changing shifts urged the drills on without ceasing; skilled timberers followed up the attack on the breast and covered the heads of the assailants like shield-bearers.

"The dump at the mouth of the tunnel grew rapidly to the proportions of an artificial plateau raised above the surrounding valley slope; yet the speed of the electric currents which exploded the blasts scarcely kept pace with the impatient anxiety of the tunnel owners to reach the lode, when the extent of the great Consolidated Virginia Bonanza was reported; for every ton raised from the lode was a loss to them of two dollars, as they thought.

"Urged on by zeal, pride, and natural covetousness, the miners cut their way indomitably towards the goal, though, at every step gained the work grew more painful and more dangerous.

"The temperature at the face of the heading, had risen from 72° (Fahr.) at the close of the year 1873 to 83° during the two following years; though in the summer of 1875 two powerful Root blowers were constantly employed in forcing air into the tunnel. At the close of the year 1876, the indicated temperature was 90° and, on the 1st of January, 1878, the men were working in a temperature of 96°.

"In spite of the air currents from the blowers, the atmosphere before the end of the year 1876 had become almost unbearably foul as well as hot. The candles flickered with a dull light and men often staggered back from their posts, faint and sickened.

"During the months preceding the junction with the Savage Mine, the heading was cut with almost passionate eagerness. The miners were then two miles from the nearest ventilating shaft, and the heat of their working chamber was fast growing too intense for human endurance.

"The pipe which applied compressed air to the drills was opened at several points and the blowers were worked to their utmost capacity. Still the mercury rose from 98° on the 1st of March 1878 to 109° on the 22nd of

April, and the temperature of the rock face of the heading increased from 110° to 114°. Four shifts a day were worked instead of three, and the men could only work during a small portion of their nominal hours of labor.

"Even the tough, wiry mules of the car train could hardly be driven up to the end of the tunnel and sought for fresh air not less ardently than the men. Curses, blows, and kicks could scarcely force them away from the blower-tube openings, and, more than once, a rationally obstinate mule thrust his head in the end of the canvas air-pipe. He was literally torn away by main strength, as the miners, when other means failed, tied his tail to the bodies of two other mules in his train and forced them to haul back their companion, snorting viciously, and slipping with stiff legs over the wet floor.

"Neither men nor animals could long endure work so distressing. Fortunately, the compressed air drills knew neither weariness nor pain, and churned their way to the mines without ceasing.

"A blast from the Savage Mine tore an opening through the wall, in the evening of that day. The goal for which Sutro had striven so many years was in sight. He was waiting at the breach, impatient of delay, and crawled, half-naked, through the jagged opening, while the foul air of the heading was still gushing into the mine."

Meanwhile, over the heads of the workers of the Sutro tunnel, a not less marvelous change had come over the Comstock Lode. This was the discovery of the Great Bonanza. After the slump of 1864 and the terrible handicap of the water, mine-owners on the Comstock fell deeper and deeper into despair. Gone were the wild days of riot and extravagance. Only by extreme care, by the use of every modern appliance, by the lowering of wages — some thirty pitched battles, with six-shooters, marked this period — were they able to keep going at all.

Then, just as two Irishmen had first found the Comstock, two other Irishmen forged to the front. These were John W. Mackay, who had begun work as a day-laborer in the mine, and James G. Fair, a young fellow who had come to Virginia City with only a few hundred dollars' capital. They made a daring team. Seizing the opportunities of the dull times, they bought property after property as it was abandoned by the owners, who declared that the great lode had "pinched out." With a third Irishman, Wm. O'Brien, and a 'Frisco miner, James C. Flood, they bought the entire stretch between the two famous mines—the Ophir and the Gould & Curry—thus forming what became known to history as the Virginia Consolidated. The four men paid $50,000 for this huge property; risking their all on the chance that deeper mining might reach the supposedly "pinched out" vein.

They sank a shaft, down, down and down,—nothing! They ran a drift to meet it from one of their purchased mines, and drilled for weeks—nothing! Then a thin seam of ore appeared, but so small as to seem insignificant. Fair pursued this vein. A quarter of a million dollars were eaten up in chasing this elusive line of ore but the vein would neither disappear nor get wider. Fair's partners tried to insist on running galleries in various directions to explore—and did so for one month while he was ill—but Fair returned insistently again to that thin thread of silver. There was one place where it was only two inches thick. And then, in October 1873, the miners cut suddenly into the Big Bonanza.

"No discovery," wrote Lord, "to match this one had ever been made on this earth from the time when the first miner struck a ledge with his rude pick. The plain facts are as marvelous as a Persian tale, for the young Aladdin did not see in the glittering cave of the genii such fabulous riches as were lying in the dark womb of the rock.

"The wonder grew as the depths were searched out foot by foot. The Bonanza was cut at a point 1167 feet below the surface, and, as the shaft went down, it was pierced again at the 1200-foot level. One hundred feet deeper and the prying pick and drill told the same story, yet another hundred feet, and the mass appeared to be swelling. When, finally, the 1500-foot level was reached and ore richer than any before met with was disclosed, the fancy of the coolest brains ran wild. How far this great Bonanza would extend, none could predict, but its expansion seemed to keep pace with the most sanguine imaginings. To explore it thoroughly was to cut it out bodily; systematic search through it was a continual revelation."

124

The wealth revealed was beyond believing. This Bonanza, alone, yielded $3,000,000 of silver every month for the first three years.

Yet it was hard to win. Mackay believed in high wages and paid more than double the wages given to any miners in any place in the history of the world. All were picked men, who had passed a severe medical test. The hours were short. The men worked naked save for a loin-cloth and shoes to protect them from the hot rocks. The heat reached 110°. Three men, who stepped accidentally into a deep pool of water, were scalded to death. The air was foul. The toil was severe.

Yet ever, the deeper they went, the richer grew the ore. When, at last, Mackay, Fair, O'Brien, and Flood sold their holdings, the Bonanza had yielded more than $150,000,000 worth of silver, one-third of which had passed directly into the pockets of the four men.

But what of the first discoverers, McLaughlin and Riley? They had found the silver, but the Bonanza was not for them. McLaughlin worked for a while as a laborer and then was thrown out of the mine by a foreman who said he was too old. He tried a dozen small ventures and not only lost in everything he touched, but caused his partners to lose, also. Bad fortune dogged him steadily. An old man, worn out and hopelessly dispirited, died in a hospital and was buried in a pauper's grave. Later, it was learned that this was McLaughlin.

O'Riley fared no better. He refused to work for others, believing that luck would turn, and that he, who had once discovered so rich a prize, would, some day or other, discover another. One night, in a dream, he heard what he took to be the voices of the fairies of the mountain bidding him dig at a certain barren spot on the hill-slopes of the Sierras, many miles away from the Comstock Lode.

For days, for weeks, for years, he dug, ever hearing the fancied voices leading him on, deeper and deeper still. Mackay offered him money, but O'Riley refused to accept it, demanding that he be given an equal share in the mine, or nothing. He starved and suffered, sometimes finding pieces of pure silver and pure gold in his tunnel, which he ascribed to his fairies (but which rumor says Mackay had arranged to be placed there) and, in old age, his tunnel fell in and crippled him. From the hospital he was taken to an insane asylum, where he died.

Henry Comstock met the fate he deserved. For years he swaggered about Virginia City claiming to be its founder and the discoverer of the Comstock Lode, living on the charity of luckier men who threw him a bar of silver as one throws a bone to a dog, or else selling wild-cat shares to greenhorns. More than once he was justly accused of being in league with the disorderly elements of the city and having taken part in robberies. But a certain rough sense of pity kept him from being strung up to a tree as he deserved a dozen times over—and he died, at last, a suicide.

CHAPTER IX
WHERE TREASURE HIDES

"You won't be achin', none, to hear all o' my roamin's after I quit the Sutro Tunnel," Jim resumed, a couple of days later, when Owens and Clem came to hear the rest of his story, "so I'll cut 'em short. But you'll be wantin' to hear how it was I got into that queer part o' the country where I made my strike.

"It was Father's doin's more'n it was mine. I reckon I'd ha' stuck around the Comstock Lode an' got into reg'lar silver-quartz minin' if I'd gone my own way. But Father didn't have no use for silver. He was a gold prospector, he was, an' he didn't want to do nothin' else.

"After the Comstock got goin' good, with big stamp-mills poundin' an' roarin' night an' day, an' when Virginia City begun to settle into a sure-enough town, Father begun to itch to be away. Folks worried him. Gold, he used to say, had savvy enough to hide itself when a mob come around, an', accordin' to Father's ideas, a placer wasn't no good, anyhow, after two seasons' pickin's.

"He jest wanted to come along an' skim off the cream o' some new find, clean up enough dust to keep him goin' for a while, an' then pick up his stakes an' git! It wasn't jest the money Father was after. He liked huntin' after gold, jest for the sake o' huntin'. I've seen him quit a claim that was makin' a fair profit an' start off prospectin', for the sake o' the change. The wilder the spot, the more chance there was o' findin' gold, he used to say; the fewer the folks, the bigger the clean-up. Looked like he was right, too, placer fields peter out mighty fast when a gang gets there."

"They are bound to," Owens agreed.

"But why? There ain't no rule about gold. One placer'll give up millions in dust, an' another ain't worth pannin'."

"There's no rule that will tell you where to find placer gold," the mine-owner corrected, "but don't run away with the idea that gold deposits are all freaks. As a matter of fact, there is a regular science to help a good prospector in hunting for reef or quartz gold. Whether he will find it in sufficient quantity to make the deposit worth working is quite another matter.

"You mustn't think, Jim, that gold happens to be in one place and happens not to be in another as a result of mere chance. There's no chance in Nature. We think there is, sometimes, merely because the factors are so terribly complicated that we can't follow them all.

"What makes the finding of gold seem so much a matter of luck is not because we don't know how the gold came to be where it is, but because we can't know the whole history of the Earth before Man came, and we can't read everything from the rocks which crop out on the surface. But we have some clues, and if you studied out the big money-making gold-mines of to-day, you would find that chance has played but a small part in their discovery and no part at all in their working.

"A lucky prospector may have been the first to find signs of gold in the region, but most likely, he got but little out of it. It was the scientific search which followed that revealed the location of the great rock deposits below in which the gold was thinly scattered, and it was highly specialized mining engineering which made them possible to work. There are mines where ores containing only two dollars' worth of gold (48 grains, a tenth of an ounce) to the ton are successfully handled, and the greater part of the big gold-mines run along quite comfortably on five dollars' worth."

"You mean on a quarter of an ounce o' gold to the ton!" exclaimed Jim, amazed. "I've often got ten times that much in one pan!"

"Exactly. Yet you're not a millionaire, are you? Most gold-mines run on a narrow margin of profit, a dollar or two to the ton of ore crushed. So, you see, the works must be on a huge scale in order to return a dividend on the investment. What's more, you can't afford to establish a big plant unless there's an enormous amount of ore available.

"It's an old rule of wise investors not to put money into a mine that looks too rich. Why?

"Because rich ore generally peters out fast. The rich mines always catch the suckers easily, and they're the ones who lose. A few cents a ton profit on an immense deposit of low-grade ore means a sure return, because, as a rule, such ore comes from a very old geological formation where the gold is evenly scattered, and labor-saving machinery can be put in with a certainty that those few cents of profit will continue indefinitely.

"Gold, as you know, Jim, is always the same price. This has been agreed upon by all nations. It is the one standard of value. It is worth a fraction over $20 an ounce. Year in, year out, all over the world, gold is worth the same.

"As a result, a gold-mine manager who knows the exact proportion of gold per ton in the ore of his mine, can calculate to a cent how much he can afford to pay for mining the ore, crushing it, and separating the gold by chemical processes. He must figure on the cost of installing his machinery, on his interest for original outlay, on depreciation, on the cost of power for his machinery, on the water power needed for crushing and washing, on transportation for his supplies and on wages. Usually he will have to build his own railroad and his own aqueducts. A little saving in one place — even a few cents per ton — will enable him to make a big profit; a little extra cost, such as an increase in the price of fuel, of chemicals, or of wages, will make him bankrupt.

"That is why, Jim, even the richest-ored mine in the world — if it be uneven in its yield of gold per ton — may be worthless, and why a low-grade mine with an unchanging percentage may be worth millions, so long as there is plenty of it. It all depends on the cost of extracting the metal. There are scores, yes, hundreds of gold-deposits well known to-day, which cannot be worked as long as gold stays $20 an ounce, because it costs almost as much as that to get it out, but which would be big money-makers if the gold were worth $25. Three-quarters of the gold-mines of to-day would shut tight like a clam, if gold were to drop in price even a dollar or two. What a capitalist wants to-day is ore, and he is not interested in free gold. What a prospector looks for, is free gold, and he ignores the rock. I'm telling you all this, now, Jim, because it's what will be the important thing when we get to talking, later, over your find."

"That's all right," the old prospector answered, "but how can a man tell when he's tappin' a big lot o' rock or jest a little, if it ain't the free gold what shows him?"

"He can't tell, as a rule," the mine-owner rejoined. "It takes a geologist to do that. As I was saying, there are some rules to go by. Here, I'll give you a notion of how gold came to be in the rocks, and then you'll see what a geologist can tell and what he can't.

"To start with, you've got to begin 'way at the beginning of things, before the crust of the earth was solid and when all the rocks of the crust were in a melted and half-liquid state. So far as we can make out, the metals seems to have classified themselves at that time, more or less, according to density. The lighter elements came to the surface, the heavier ones stayed at the bottom. It wasn't merely a question of weight, but of gravitation, centrifugal action and a lot of things I won't stop to explain to you now. Gold, as you know, is heavy, that is, it possesses extreme density. It stayed therefore, mainly at the bottom of this semi-molten sea.

"But this sea, which covered the whole of the earth's surface, wasn't altogether liquid, as the oceans are to-day. It was a seething mass of different densities, some of it liquid, some of it slimy, some of it thick like sticky mud, acted upon by fearful whirlwinds of electric forces such as astronomers see in the sun to-day, and by powerful internal currents which created vast churning whirlpools of super-heated matter.

"It's impossible for us to tell where these electric whirlwinds passed or where these currents were. So, since the original separation of the metals was highly irregular, no geologist can say with certainty where gold or silver, lead or tin, will be found in the greatest quantity.

"Then there's another complication. As you know, most of the metals have chums or affinities with other substances, just as gold has with mercury. These chums of the metals were also in that molten ocean, but not always in the same proportions, nor yet distributed regularly. So metallic compounds were formed at different times and in diverse places. These compounds had varying densities, with the result that in later ages they behaved in a way quite different from the pure metal. You see, Jim, long before the crust of the earth was even formed, gold was scattered far and wide, and already was in different forms.

"Then, little by little, the crust began to form as the earth cooled. It was just a scum, at first, and was constantly broken up from below. As it got thicker, it resisted more and more, until the upheavals of the crust formed the mountains of the earliest or Primary Age. This crust, which was now solid rock, contained gold, but, naturally, nowhere in the same proportions. Some had much metal inclusion; some, little; some, none at all. Besides, between the mountains or in them, were vast volcanic craters, pouring up molten matter which became what are known as the eruptive rocks, and these, too, carried up gold from below. These rocks crystallized and the gold remained in them.

"But even that wasn't complicated enough for Mother Nature. In those same eruptive rocks, both of the early and later periods, gold is mainly found in veins. These veins are of dozens of different sorts, depending on the rock in which they occur and on Nature's ways of putting them there.

"To make it simple to you, I'll only mention two. The most general method was by fumaroles. These are subterranean blow-holes of vapor containing sulphur, tellurium, and chlorine compounds, as well as super-heated steam. These vapors, projected from deep down in the earth with incredible pressure and energy, acted on the new-made rocks, formed compounds with the metals, or, when united with hydrogen in the steam, separated the metals from solutions of their salts, and forced the metals into cracks in the new-made and cooling eruptive rocks. According to the kind of rock and the nature of the chemical agent, a geologist will know for what type of vein to search. The other most general agent of vein-making was hot water—generally heavily saturated with sulphur and other chemicals—which dissolved the gold. This hot water, with gold in solution, seeped into the cracks and crevices made by the rock as it cooled, thus forming other types of veins."

"Hold on a minute, there!" protested Jim. "Water won't dissolve gold."

"It will and does," was the retort, "especially when certain chemicals are in the water. As a matter of fact, even to-day, the geysers at Steamboat

Springs, California, and at several places in New Zealand, deposit gold and silicon in their basins. But let me go on.

"After the gold was placed in veins in these primary rocks, there came a period of erosion, and the mountains were worn away. The gold being harder than rock, it remained and made alluvial deposits of a very early age. Some, of these old 'placers' are several miles below the surface, now, others have come again to the surface by all the superposed rock having been washed away, anew. Some of the gold was dissolved, as before, and got into the crevices of the newly deposited rocks made by erosion, known as sedimentary rocks. So, you see, Jim, even millions of years ago, there was gold in the crystallized eruptive rock, gold in veins of igneous rock, gold in alluvial deposits, and, again, gold in veins in the sedimentary rocks.

"Then came another period of elevation, with a second raising up of mountain ranges, and with a renewal of violent volcanic action. The crust was getting more and more unequal, the way in which the metals were distributed became more and more scattered. Mountains of the Secondary Age were often made of Primary sedimentary rocks, or of Primary igneous rocks, so much changed that geologists call them metamorphic rocks. And, Jim, every time that the rock was changed, the gold changed either its place or its compound character, or both. Then came another period of erosion, lasting millions of years, the gold was washed away to form new placers, or made its way into veins in the Secondary sedimentary rocks.

"Then came the great upheaval of the Third or Tertiary Age, in which new mountains rose, new volcanic vents were opened, and, once more, much of the gold was acted upon by chemicals, mainly sulphur and tellurium. In many places silver showed a strong affinity with gold, forming deposits where the ores were commingled. Once more the hundreds of centuries of erosion came, to be followed by the upheaving of the newer mountains of the Fourth or Quaternary Age. So, you see, Jim, as I told you before, gold can be found in almost every rock and of every geological period."

"I don't see that it helps much, then!" declared the old prospector. "You can go lookin' where you durn please."

"There's nothing to stop you," agreed Owens cheerfully, "but that's a hit-and-miss method. And I can show you just how even this little bit of geology comes in to help the miner.

"Get this clearly in your head, Jim! Three-quarters of the present gold production of the world comes from gold that is mixed with pyrites — which is a sulphide of iron, or from tellurides — in which a tellurium-hydrogen compound has been the chemical agent. A prospector, therefore, who uncovers a new field where the gold is in the pyritous or the telluride form has ten times more chance of attracting capital than one who finds lumps of native gold lying around loose.

"It is when a prospector strikes a section where all the gold-bearing rock has been eroded that he is apt to find the 'pockets' so dear to his heart. The amazing riches of the Klondyke lay in the fact that prospectors found, first, the alluvial deposits from the present age in the sands of the running creeks, and, on ledges high above the creeks and running into the rocks on either side, the alluvial deposits, even thicker and richer, of a bygone time."

"You've got it right," declared Jim, emphatically. "I know 'cos I was there!"

"Was it on the Yukon, then, that you made your famous strike?"

The prospector winced. Evidently, he intended to reach that point in his own way.

"I'll tell you about that, after a bit," he answered evasively. "But you ain't said why placer claims peter out."

"Can't you see? A placer claim doesn't show where the big store of gold is, but where it isn't! It shows that the gold has gone. A placer is just a spot where a little heavy gold, that hasn't been acted on by chemicals, happens to have been deposited during the erosion of a mountain which was composed of gold-bearing rock. The rock has been washed into sand and gravel and a great deal of it taken out to sea. There's plenty of gold in the sea, as I told you before.

"But the amount of sand or gravel to be panned along a creek or river is limited. When that's washed over, there's no more to find. A prospector gets down to bed-rock and he's through. Then he's either got to pack up and hunt some new spot where the same erosion has happened, or, if he's clever enough, he's got to find the rock or reef from which the gold was washed out. If he doesn't know his geology, he's apt to waste his time.

"Then the scientific expert and the capitalist come in. It's the man with money who profits most by a poor man's strike. He can afford to sit back and wait. Presently the expert will come back and report where the gold-bearing rock lies. The capitalist arrives with huge machinery for mining and crushing the rock, for turning on enormous water-power, in short, for performing a sort of artificial erosion in a few days which Nature took hundreds of thousands of years to do. He pockets millions, where the prospectors who did the first work only get thousands, or even hundreds, or, sometimes, nothing at all.

"Your father was perfectly right, Jim, in saying that the prizes of prospecting are for the man who gets there first. Placers are bound to peter out quickly. They are Nature's purses, and a purse hasn't any more money in it than you put in. Even the Klondyke, that astounding pocket of riches, lasted only three years and then dwindled down.

"Some of these days, all the available places of the earth will have been worked over by the casual prospector, and then his day will be done. The ever-hoping rover of the pick, shovel, and pan is becoming extinct. Even now, the only spots which hold out any chance of pockets of gold are in the almost inaccessible section of the globe.

"The daring seeker for gold must go to the bleak ranges of the frigid North, where, even in the middle of the summer, the ground is frozen as hard as a rock a few inches below the surface; or else to the jungle-clad slopes of the tropics, where fever and stewing heat menace him with ever-present death; or yet to regions so far removed from civilization that the white man has not yet penetrated there. The shores of the Arctic Ocean, the steaming equatorial forests of the Eastern Andes, or the untrodden valleys of the inner Himalayas offer the most hopes to the prospector. But he may spend all the gold-dust he finds, and more, to go there and return.

"The tundras of Alaska and eastward to Hudson Bay still contain placer gold, to a surety, gold not difficult to find if a man is willing to face an

Arctic winter and a mosquito-haunted summer to work there. It's a wonder to me, Jim, that your father didn't join the great rush to the Fraser River, in British Columbia, in 1856. That was a mad and sorrowful stampede, if ever there was one!"

"He was crazy about the Fraser," Jim answered. "All that kep' him from goin' was the smash-up o' the Kern River rush, which lef' him dead-broke an' nigh starvin', like I told you. But he never forgot the Fraser. That's what took us up north, to wind up with.

"It was in '79, when I was twenty years old, that Father comes into the cabin, an' says, point blank,

"'We're a-goin' to the Kootenay.'

"'Where's that?' I asks.

"'Somewheres up near the Fraser River. There's gold there, so they're sayin', like there was on the Sacramento in '49. An' thar ain't no one, hardly, thar! Fust one in gits it all.'

"I tried to reason with him. So did Mother, but it weren't no manner o' use. A week later, we was gone."

"I shouldn't have thought he'd have found much on the Kootenay," said Owens reflectively, "it's all vein mining there. That needs heavy crushing machinery."

"Not all," Jim corrected. "There's some glacial gravel there an' we washed out enough to pay our way. But Father wanted something bigger.

"We struck out from West Kootenay an' hit the trail for Six Mile Creek, near Kicking Horse Pass, in Upper East Kootenay. We stayed there a while, but some one, who had a grudge agin the Mormons, pulled his gun on Father. A 'forty-niner' ain't apt to be lazy on the shoot, an' Father's gun spit first. We didn't wait for the funeral, but moved on, an' lively, at that, strikin' for the Fraser."

"Good thing for you the N. W. M. P. (North West Mounted Police), didn't strike your trail!" commented Owens.

"It was a straight-enough deal," protested Jim, "an' the N. W.'s ha' got plenty o' sense. But that wasn't no reason for hangin' around, lookin' for trouble. We thought the Fraser'd be healthier. As it turned out, it wasn't.

"The Fraser boom was dead. The shacks in the ol' minin' camps was rottin' to ruin. The machinery—what little there was of it—was lyin' there, rustin'. The sluices had all fallen to bits, except on Hop Rabbit Creek. A couple o' hundred men was there still, workin' over the tailin's, but they was all Chinamen. Up the creek a ways some o' them was pannin'.

"Second day we was there, a big Chink comes up to me, an' says, very quiet like,

"'You plenty sabbee? Run away quick!'

"It didn't look that way to me, for I don't take to orderin'. I was good an' ready to drop that Chink in his tracks, but I did a little thinkin' first. Two hundred agin two is big odds. I nodded, an' the big Chink turns away.

"I didn't say nothin' about the warnin' to Father, for he was that stubborn he'd ha' waded right in an' tried to clean up the whole camp. He wouldn't ha' had the chance of a rat in a trap. He'd ha' got himself carved up in little slices an' that was about all. So I jest told him that one o' the Chinks had reported there was a new strike on the Cassiar. Father took the bait like a hungry trout an' we was off in an hour."

"But I always thought Chinamen were such a peaceful lot!" exclaimed Clem.

"If a Chink comes into a white camp, he's willin' to sing small an' do what he's told. But in a boom camp that white folks have given up an' quit, if Johnny Chink comes in, he won't let nary a white come back. I know! One o' my pardners was in the massacre o' Happy Man Gulch in '87. That's a yarn worth hearin'! I'll tell it you, some time.

"Out we trailed to the Cassiar, an', funny enough, though I'd only been bluffin' to Father about the strike there, we landed on the pay gravel the very day after French Pete had struck a pocket. He was a good prospector, was French Pete, an' knew more'n most, but he was timid like, an' glad to have us there. He could handle Indians—he was a half-breed himself—but he was that superstitious, he was afraid o' the dark, alone. He was religious, too, an' Father an' him got along together famous. We staked out a claim, right next to his, an', for a few weeks, cleaned up a good fifty dollars a day.

"Then, one fine mornin', a bunch o' redskins come down, friends o' French Pete. They palavered some, an', after a while, French Pete he comes over to us an' says:

"'We got three days to get out!'

"Father he put up an awful howl an' was for plugging the redskins full o' holes, pronto. But French Pete puts it to him that these Injuns was his friends, an' shootin' wouldn't go. There'd been some kind o' deal between this tribe an' the Chilkoots, an' every miner on the Divide knew more'n plenty about the Chilkoots. They'd tortured to death Georgie Holt, the first prospector that ever went over the Chilkoot Pass, an' more'n one miner that got into their country wasn't never heard of no more.

"So Father puts it up to French Pete where he's goin' next. French Pete is a good pardner, an' tells a queer tale, but he tells it straight. He allows there's gold on the islands off the coast an' shows the lay.

"Some years afore, so he says, Joe Juneau, an old-time Hudson Bay trapper, an' Dick Harris, one o' the forty-niners, had found color on Gold Creek, near the coast, an' had made a pile. Juneau went on prospectin', though he was rich, an', havin' a generous streak, grub-staked any man what asked him. That way he got a big share in the placers found on Silver Bow and doubled his pile. Some other prospectors what he'd grub-staked reported havin' found gold on the islands, but nothin' extraordinary. Harris, havin' a business head, stuck around Gold Creek (the present town of Juneau was formerly called Harrisburg) an' got rich a-plenty. Juneau an' Harris had more'n enough to look after, an' never got over to the islands.

"French Pete, he's an old friend of Juneau an' he knows about this island game. He reckons it'd be worth pannin'. There's sure-enough gold up thar to pay for the workin', an' there might be a chance for a big haul, seein' no one is prospectin' thar. He offers to show Father where the placers are supposed to be, if he's willin' to come along. Father likes to stick by his pardner an' agrees.

"From Cassiar we hoofed it back to Juneau — a long an' a hard trail — an', after buyin' a small sailboat an' grub enough for three months, we struck out for Douglas Island. French Pete handled that boat like a cowboy does a buckin' bronc. We was green wi' scare in that wild sea, full o' chunks o' ice clashin' all around, but the old trapper never turns a hair. Presently we landed on a beach which looked like it was a seal rookery, once, an' works our way to where a good-sized creek comes plungin' down to the sea.

"Juneau had it right. The sands along the creek were full o' color, but the dust was small an' it was slow pannin'. It was all we could do to make fourteen dollars a day in dust, workin' fourteen hours a day, maybe; poor pickin's for a spot costin' so much cash an' trouble to get to.

"French Pete, though, had plenty o' savvy. From the lie o' the rock, he reckoned this thin placer gold must ha' been washed out o' the little mountain what sticks up in one corner o' the island. He let his placer claim go for a while and prospected for ore. At last he found what he thought looked like the best spot. The ore was poor in color, but so soft an' rotten that it could be smashed into dust with a hammer, an' the gold — what little there was of it — separated out easy.

"We all staked out half-a-dozen claims, doin' enough work on each to hold title. Since French Pete had brought us to the island, an' shown the rock besides, Father an' I promised to give him a quarter o' whatever we got for our claims, if we ever sold 'em.

"Off went French Pete in the sail-boat, leavin' us marooned on Douglas Island, an' in a pickle of a mess supposin' he shouldn't return! But he come back, sure enough, after about six weeks, havin' found John Treadwell, a minin' man, who undertakes to buy our claims if Juneau, after havin' looked 'em over, says they're all right.

"Juneau an' Treadwell come, a couple o' days after, wi' one o' these up-to-date engineer Johnnies. The ore's low-grade, but there's head enough in the creek to run stamp mills by water-power, which makes cheap crushin'.

Treadwell pays French Pete $15,000 for his claims an' Father an' me $10,000 apiece. Then he buys up the rest o' the island for next to nothin'. The Treadwell mine's a big un, now, workin' 540 stamp mills, an', as Mr. Owens says, it's makin' millions out o' low grade ore.

"Father had promised Mother, as soon as he got $10,000 clear, he'd go back home. She holds him to it. After payin' French Pete what we promised, there's $10,000 for Father an' $5,000 for me, besides what was left from the Cassiar an' Douglas Island placer clean-ups. Father an' Mother went back to Utah, leavin' me wi' French Pete an' Treadwell.

"But Father couldn't stand it long. While he was prospectin', all hours, all weathers, he was tough an' strong. Back in town, he begun to pine. In less'n a year he was dead. Mother didn't live long after him. That lef' me on my own hook. Douglas Island was too slow, though Treadwell offered me a good job as long's I cared to stick it out. But I wanted to be off an' away, feelin' sure, some day, I'd make my big strike.

"I was foot-loose, now, wi' five thousand in dust an' the whole world to roam in. Where was I goin' to find the place where the sands was nothin' but gold? Somewheres, I was sure! Some day I'd strike it rich an' never have to work no more. Out in the wild beyond, where no one else was, millions was waitin' for me!"

CHAPTER X
THE ROARING NORTH

"I was young an' tough in them days an' liked to buck agin hard goin'. If gold was gettin' scarce where folks was, it was plenty an' free in the lands that folks didn't dare go to. Naturally enough, I begun to think o' the Chilkoot country.

"Ever since Georgie Holt had been tortured to death in a Chilkoot Indian camp, prospectors had been leery o' that huntin' ground. But French Pete had heard from a pard o' Juneau's that Dumb MacMillan had got over the Chilkoot an' struck it rich on what he called Dumb Creek, runnin' into the Tanana. He'd come back an' cashed his dust, blowed it in on one wild spree, an' gone over the Pass again. He hadn't never been heard of no more.

"Since his second trip, though, the Canadian Government had got a strangle-hold on the Chilkoots an' was makin' 'em behave. It had forced 'em to make peace wi' the Stick Indians o' the interior, an' thrown the fear o' the whites into 'em good an' plenty. So I wasn't worryin' over Injuns none. The Chilkoot Pass, though, was said to be something awful to cross, but that wasn't goin' to stop me, when I knew there was good goin' on the other side an' all the creeks full o' gold.

"So I quit Treadwell an' French Pete an' got back to Juneau. There, I heard that a bunch o' prospectors led by the Schiefflin Brothers had taken a steamboat, got as far as St. Michael, gone up the Yukon, wintered at Nuklukayet an' found gold all the way. They'd struck good placers on Mynook, Hess an' Shevlin Creeks, but the Schiefflins found the ground always frozen an' terrible hard to work, an' the summer was so short they figured pannin' on the Yukon wouldn't pay.

"Think o' that, will you! The Klondyke an' the Eldorado wouldn't pay!

"That same summer, we heard that there was new gold strikes on the Lewes an' Big Salmon Rivers, which run into the Upper Yukon. Dumb MacMillan had found payin' color on the Tanana, flowin' into the Middle Yukon. The Schiefflins had located plenty o' placers on the Lower Yukon.

"It didn't take much figurin' to guess that there was gold all the way along. I made up my mind to strike over the Chilkoot into the Stewart River section, jest about unknown then; preparin', durin' the winter, for an early start.

"Early in the spring o' '84, eight of us was ready. We had a sure-enough outfit an' plenty o' grub. We was well fixed for shootin'-irons, too, for we was goin' up into hostile Injun country.

"Joe Juneau, who knew a lot about the mountains, tried to head us off, tellin' what happened to Holt an' MacMillan, but we was sot on goin', an' struck out for Dyea along the canal trail. There we headed for the interior.

"I've seen some rough goin' in my time, an' I come of a stock o' tough uns, but, I'm tellin' you, that first trip over the Chilkoot Pass was more'n horrible. I dream about it, yet — an' it's over thirty years ago!

"From Dyea to Sheep Camp was bad enough goin', half-frozen muskeg (mucky swamp), lyin' under soft snow an' all covered with a tangle o' thorn-vines climbin' over spraggly berry-bushes. There warn't no trail. It was cut your way, an' drag! We didn't have no dogs, but lugged the sleighs ourselves. It's only nine miles as the crow flies, but it took us four days to make it, with our loads.

"An' then the Chilkoot Pass stuck up in front of us, all black rock an' white snow, reachin' to the sky, an' clouds hidin' the top. It seemed like it was a-defyin' of us, well-nigh impossible.

"We'd ha' gone back, sure, but we knew two men had climbed it a'ready, Georgie Holt in '72, and Dumb MacMillan, in '80. What they'd done, we reckoned we could do.

"Sheer rock, she was, all slick an' icy, to begin with; above that, stretches o' snow-fields on so steep a slope that a false step meant a snow-slide an' good-bye! crevasses in the snow goin' down below all knowin', an' mostly covered over wi' light snow so's you couldn't see 'em; an', near the top, a pile o' loose an' shaky rocks built up like a wall, straight as the side of a house, an', in some spots, leanin' over. That was the Chilkoot Pass!

"The cold was cruel; a steady wind, nigh to a blizzard, sucked through the Pass continooal, tearin' a man from his footin.' There was no shelter, an' high up, no fire-wood.

"There was no trail, neither! We had to go it, blind. An', up that rock, over them snow-fields, across them crevasses, an', fly-like, crawling up that wall o' bowlders, we had to drag our dunnage! The sleighs had to be pulled up, empty. Our sacks o' flour had to be toted on our backs! An' our bacon an' groceries, enough to last us months! An' our tools an' cradles! I made five trips to get my stuff across—an it took me five weeks. Between whiles, I rested, if lyin' exhausted means rest!

"There was eight of us that started. There was only three when the stuff was on the summit o' the pass! Two had been crushed by fallin' rocks. The other three had all disappeared sudden in a crevasse, what they thought was solid snow givin' down under 'em. Only Red Bill, Bull Evans an' me was left.

"Mind, there was no trail an' no guide! Holt had been over years before, but the Indians killed him. Dumb MacMillan went over it twice, an' never was heard of no more. Me an' my pardners was the third, an', as I was sayin', o' the eight that started, only three got to the top."

"Yet how many thousands climbed that Pass after gold had been struck on the Klondyke?" queried Owens.

"Thirty thousand an' more, so folks said. Two thousand o' them, though, died in tryin'. An' they had Injun an' half-breed porters to tote their dunnage, too! The trail was marked for them. In the last years o' the big rush, there was an aerial tramway to take up the stuff. It wasn't like that in my day. We tackled it on our own.

"When we reached the top, the trouble wasn't over neither. 'Tother side was rough an' dangerous, all loose rock an' mighty little snow. We loaded the sleighs an' let 'em down by jerks, all three men hangin' on to the drag-ropes. But we made the bottom, safe, an' started off again. No trail, no map, no nothin'! We jest pushed on, blind, three white men in a country o' hostile Injuns huntin' for a river which we didn't even know where it was.

"Followin' a small creek an' pannin' now an' agin—though not findin' any color—we came at last to Crater Lake an' then on to Lindeman, an' final, to Lake Bennett. Here, we'd heard before leavin', the Yukon River begun, an' we started to go round the lake, so's to strike the bank o' the river.

"It couldn't be done. Muskeg an' thick forest run clear down to the shore o' the lake, an' a b'ar couldn't ha' pushed his way through. Small creeks shot out every which way. Sleighs were worse'n useless.

"There warn't nothin' to be done but build a boat, an' nary one o' the three of us knew the fust durn thing about boat-buildin'. But we put together a kind of a log-raft, that floated, anyway, put the dunnage aboard it, an' drifted down the lake. This was easy goin', for a while.

"All of a sudden, a swift current took us, the lake narrowed into a river, an', afore we had a chance to pole our heavy an' clumsy raft to the bank, we was shootin' wi' sickenin' speed down white water. It was Grand Canyon Rapids, a mile long! Half-way through, the raft struck a rock an' went to bits, the logs bustin' free. I grabbed one an' went spinnin' down the rapids. I must ha' hit my head on a snag, for I don't remember no more till I woke up to find myself on the bank, an' Bull Evans leanin' over me.

"'What's the worst, Bull?' I asks, as soon as I realizes.

"'Red Bill's gone,' he says, 'an' so's most o' the grub. The dunnage is scattered anywheres along a mile or two. We hoofs it from here. No more rafts in mine!'

"An' a good thing we did hoof it, too. If we'd got through the Grand Canyon Rapids an' struck, unknowin', the White Horse Rapids—what they afterwards called the 'Miners' Grave'—nary a one o' the three of us would ha' come out alive.

"As it was, bein' afoot, we broke away from what afterwards was the Klondyke Trail, an', instead of striking across Lake Labarge, kep' between it an' Lake Kluane, strikin' some creeks leadin' into the White River. There, at last, after three months on the trail, we panned an' found color. We trailed on, pannin' as we went, cleanin' up pretty fair, an' final, struck some placers on the Stewart River. The Injuns was peaceful an' we could get grub from a half-breed tradin' store near old Fort Selkirk. We wintered there."

"That was in '85?" Owens queried.

"Winter o' '85 an' spring o' '86."

"Then you must have been right on hand for the great strike on Forty-Mile?"

"We sure was."

"But, man, you should have made a fortune, there!"

"I did!" came Jim's laconic answer.

"Well?"

"I made a hundred thousand dollars in three months."

"What happened to it, then?"

"That," said the old prospector, leaning back, and looking at his two hearers, "is a wild an' woolly yarn! Do you want to hear it, or do I go on to the findin' o' that ore you've got in your hand?"

"Oh, tell the yarn, Jim!" pleaded Clem, who was less interested in Jim's strike than was the mine-owner. Owens nodded assent.

"Pannin' gold," Jim began, "is pretty much the same all over. One minin' camp is a good deal like another, though Forty-Mile was the cleanest an' straightest camp I ever struck. I could spin a good many yarns o' Forty-Mile an' near-by camps, but I'll leave 'em to another time an' tell you how it was I got poor, again, all in a hurry.

"With a bunch o' buckskin bags holdin' a hundred thousand dollars in the coarse nuggety gold o' Forty-Mile, I was good an' ready to take the back trail. I thought maybe I'd get back again next spring, for I'd become a sure-enough 'sour-dough' (old-timer of the northern gold-fields, so-called from camp bread). But I wanted to eat heavy an' lie soft for a while. I'd spend one winter in 'Frisco, any way, an' have a run for my money.

"The more I thought of it, the less I liked the notion o' goin' back over the Chilkoot Pass. Savin' for the first climb, the out trail was worse'n the in. All the rapids'd have to be portaged.

"What was more, the news o' the Forty-Mile strike had reached the outside, an' the human buzzards was a-flockin' in. The Canadian authorities held the camps in a tight grip, but the trail was a No-Man's-Land. A sour-dough comin' out from a strike stood a good chance o' bein' plugged for his gold an' no one the wiser.

"A few weeks after the Forty-Mile strike, a rich placer had been located at Circle, a hundred miles lower down on the Yukon an' across the Alaskan Boundary jest above where Circle City is now. Nothin' was easier'n to buy a small row-boat an' float down the Yukon to Circle. The rapids wasn't worth speakin' about. At Circle we'd take the river craft runnin' to Fort Yukon, an' then ship on board the steamer for St. Michael, Skagway an' 'Frisco.

"No weary miles o' hoofin' it on the trail, no portages, no work, jest sit in a boat an' take it easy! That hundred thousand made me feel too lazy to move.

"We got the boat, bein' willin' to pay whatever fancy price was asked. While she was still tied up at Forty-Mile, one o' the North West Mounted Police come up an' asked us where we was headin'. We told him. He wanted to know how many were goin'. There was my pardner, Bull Evans, me, an' four more. He shakes his head.

"'That's about twenty too few,' says he. 'Are you takin' the dust along?'

"'Right with us, Johnny,' says we.

"'You've got more gold'n you have sense,' he comes back, cheerfully. 'Better wait a month or so. We're goin' to convoy a party through the White Pass to Skagway, takin' the express an' the bank gold, an' you can come along, safe.'

"'It's too long a trail for millionaires,' says we.

"'A dead millionaire ain't worth much,' he says. 'You'll have your bones picked clean by the crows if you get across the border that a-way. Alaska ain't the Dominion, not by a long shot.'

"That hit us wrong. We thought he was jest bluffin', tryin' to make out that Canada was the only country that could run things right. Most of us was from the U. S., an' we grouched at his pokin' in.

"'Law an' order's as good 'tother side o' the line as it is here!' says Bull.

"'Have it your own way! I'll send the patrol boat with you as far as the border. I can't do no more.'

"We didn't want the patrol, but he sent it, any way, an' we started out.

"'Last chance!' he yells, when the border's reached, 'better come back!'

"'We ain't quitters!' Bull shouts back, an' on we go, six of us, an' close on to half a million dollars in dust among the lot. Every man had a rifle, a six-shooter, an' plenty o' ammunition. All was old-timers an' quick on the shoot. We reckoned we could take care of ourselves, good an' plenty. Any way, we weren't goin' to land anywheres until we struck Circle, so there wouldn't be no danger.

"We hadn't got more'n ten miles the other side o' the line, jest beyond the little minin' camp of Eagle, when of a sudden:

"'Spat!'

"A bullet strikes the boat, right at the water line, an' she begins to leak.

"It was pretty shootin', an' every man reaches for his gun. There's a curl o' smoke driftin' up from a pile o' rock, but no one shoots, knowin' well the marksman's under cover. We trims the boat, to keep the hole out o' water, and then:

"'Spat! Spat!'

"One on each side. We stuffs some bits o' rag in the holes, but the boat begins to fill. One side o' the river's sheer rock, an' there ain't no landin' there. Cussin' free, an' every man wi' his rifle ready, we beaches the boat on the other shore an' gets out, ready for the scrap.

"Then some one starts to talk, over our heads, hidden in the rocks:

"'Gents, I'm sure sorry to stop your trip! There's twenty of us, an' each has his man covered. It ain't no use for you to make trouble. Them as is reasonable can leave their bags o' dust an' their pop-guns on the beach, an' walk off fifty paces to the left. Them as wants to show their shootin' can wait jest two minutes by the watch, an' the fun'll begin, us havin' the pick o' the shots an' bein' under cover. The cards is stacked agin you, gents, an' there ain't no use to play.'

"We all shoots back, o' course, more to relieve our feelin's'n anything else, for we knows this new-style road-agent has dodged back to cover.

"Me an' four others, we don't hesitate. We lays our bags o' dust an' our guns on the beach an' toddles off, as directed. Then I looks back an' sees Bull standin' there, alone.

"He's a durn fool an' I knows it. But he's my pardner, is Bull!

"I goes back an' tries to persuade him to eat crow. But Bull's stubborn as a mule an' don't budge. I ain't a-goin' to leave him. So we both stands there.

"The road-agent has been takin' this in, an' presently he pipes up:

"'Very pretty, gents. Pardners is pardners and that's doin' it handsome. Put up your hands an' we won't shoot.'

"For answer, Bull snaps his rifle to his shoulder an' fires.

"A volley rings out, an' Bull drops dead, a dozen bullets through him. I wasn't two yards away, but not a shot touched me.

"Then this road-agent, a tall thin galoot, heavily masked, comes down to where I'm standin' alone.

"'It was a dirty bit o' shootin'!' says I, indignant.

"'You've no cause to complain,' says he, 'nothin' hit you! I like your spunk in standin' by your pardner. He seems to ha' been a he-man, too, even if he was a fool. Had he any folks?'

"'A baby girl back in Montana,' I tells him.

"'I'm not robbin' babies,' he says to that. 'She gets my share o' the loot. I give my word. Do you know the address?'

"I reaches down into Bull's coat, takes a letter from it what he'd written to his sister, what was lookin' after the kid, an' hands this bandit the envelope. He reads it, nods an' puts it in his pocket."

"Did he ever send the money?" suddenly interrupted Owens.

"He did. I heard, years after, that the sister received thirty thousand dollars in cash, in a registered letter, sent from Skagway, an' in the envelope a slip o' paper 'From the Chief o' Circle.'"

"What happened next, Jim?" queried Clem, excitedly.

"What, after I'd given the galoot the envelope? He makes a sign an' half a dozen o' his gang comes down out o' the rocks where they've been hidin'. They gather up the guns an' the bags o' dust lyin' on the beach, while some more o' them goes over an' searches the other four men.

"'What's the next turn?' I asks the chief.

"'I don't do things in a small way,' he says. 'Your nerve's good. For bein' willin' to stand by your pardner, when the rest run like rabbits. I'll leave you five thousand in dust, an' see you get back to the border. Unless you want to join our band?'

"'I don't!' I answers, snappy like.

"But he was as good as his word. He weighs out an' hands over the dust, an' two of the gang takes me back to the line. There they gives me back my shootin'-irons, though, o' course without any ammunition. Next day I'm back in Forty-Mile."

"And the other four men?" queried Owens.

"Two joined the gang, an' later, started to get funny on the Canadian side. A Vigilance committee strung 'em up. The other two turned up at Circle City and I never heard no more about 'em.

"I staked out another claim—though there wasn't much to choose from, then—an' begins to pan again. But the luck had turned, an' I didn't strike nothin' rich.

"I stayed at Forty-Mile that winter, buildin' fires at night on the frozen dirt to thaw it, an', next day, shovelin' an' haulin' it up to the top o' my little shaft on the windlass I'd made myself. The pile o' pay dirt had to be left till the spring thaws for cleanin' up.

"Ten years I stayed inside, goin' from one placer on the Yukon to another, makin' a livin', an' that's about all. Now an' again, when I gets a bit ahead, I sends a bag o' dust to Bull's little gal.

"In '98, I joins the rush to Nome, an' there's a roarin' wild town! But luck ain't runnin' my way. Like the rest, I starts to wash the sand o' the sea-beach, the last place a prospector'd ever look. I clean up thirty a day, maybe, jest enough to keep goin'. I'm no richer'n no poorer'n I was ten years afore, but I got Bull's little gal to work for, an' that keeps me pluggin'.

"Then, sudden, I gets a letter from the gal, enclosin' a note she's received. It's short:

"'Rich pay gravel here.' It's signed with a circle, an' a cross. On the back, there's a map.

"I figures this is the Road-Agent o' Circle, an' he's dyin' an' wants to make restitootion. It's my dooty to Bull's little gal to go an' find the place. I've jest about money enough to go there, an' the lay is right. There's a bank of pay gravel more'n two miles long, an' a hundred feet deep, maybe more. It's frozen, summer'n' winter, an' too hard for thawin' with wood fires."

Jim halted for emphasis and looked keenly at the mine-owner.

"I was thawin' it out wi' coal, when I was there," he said, slowly, "soft, smudgy coal, brown an' sticky-like."

"What!" cried Owens in amazement. "Lignite coal?"

"Not a mile away from the gravel."

"But why, man—?" Owens stopped.

"A bunch o' Russian seal-poachers come up an' chased me off, sayin' it was Russian territory. I believed 'em, at first. I didn't say nothin' about the gold, but made believe I was huntin' coal. But that lignite, as you call it, was so sure low-grade that they jest laughed at me.

"It ain't in Russian territory. It's in the United States, I've found out that much. But minin' men don't take much stock in what I tell 'em, an' coal men say it's too long a haul. But a man wi' money what knows coal an' knows gold, an' could do some steam thawin' an' hydraulickin' would make good."

Owens looked at him thoughtfully.

"It's a wild and woolly yarn, all right," he said, "and it sounds like a story from a book, with the hold-up, and the girl and the idea of restitution, and the treasure-map and all the rest of it. You haven't any proof?"

"Nothin' but what I've told you—an' the map. My pardner's got to take my say-so."

"You say you wrote frequently to Bull Evans' daughter?"

"Once a season—sometimes twice. Whenever I could get some money through."

"She will have kept those letters, certainly," the mine-owner mused, "and the payments through the Express Company will be easy to trace. Where does the girl live?"

"In Pittsburgh, now, with her aunt."

"If I guarantee to advance two hundred thousand, when satisfied that your story is straight, will you produce the map and come along, yourself?"

Jim looked him over.

"I'll trust you more'n you're willin' to trust me," he said, and took a thin slip of paper from the buckskin tube out of which he had shaken the gold dust the day before. "Here's the map. It's an island due north o' the Diomede Islands in the Behring Sea. The Eskimos call it Chuklook. There's quartz gold on Ingalook, too. But mind, one-third o' what you pay for the claim belongs to Bull's little gal."

"Agreed!" declared Owens. "You trust me an' I'll trust you. The letters an' the express records, being as you say, I'll go in."

"Clem bein' a pardner!" Jim insisted.

"Clem being a partner, sure!"

CHAPTER XI
THE LONELY ISLAND

The little Bunting, brigantine-rigged, and, yacht-fashion, possessing an auxiliary screw, plowed the waters of Behring Sea.

Jim, with Clem and Anton beside him, stood on the foc's'le head, gazing into the foggy distance. Owens was on the poop, with the owner of the tiny yacht, who was a personal friend, and moodily scanned the horizon. Otto, utterly disregarding the universal sea injunction: "Don't Talk to the Man at the Wheel!" stayed at the stern and exchanged occasional sentences with the helmsman.

There were, also, two other passengers on board, both down in the cabin. One was a grizzled giant, the other was a young woman, some 25 years of age. The first was a half-brother of Joe Juneau, and was known throughout the Far North as "The Arctic Wizard" from his uncanny knowledge of Alaskan mining deposits, and his ability as a mining engineer in overcoming the peculiar difficulties of frozen ground and of maintaining machinery in working order under the most rigorous conditions of weather. The second was "Bull's little gal," more properly known as Jameine Evans, herself a graduate of the Pittsburgh School of Mines.

With the money that had been sent her, when a baby, by the Road-Agent of Circle, and with the additional sums forwarded from time to time by Jim, Jameine (so christened as a namesake of the old prospector) had been able to pay her way through school and college and had taken a mining course besides.

This specialized education had been her plan of gratitude. Only by making herself efficient in a kindred field, she felt, could she ever be a real "pardner" to Jim; only thus could she repay, in some measure, the generosity of the old prospector. She had long realized the unselfishness of the man who had stayed winter after winter in the frozen North, denying himself the rude pleasures of a mining camp in order to help "Bull's little gal."

Ever since Jim had made his famous strike, as a result of the map which had been sent to her by her father's murderer, Jameine had regarded herself as the heiress of a dream mine, but a dream which might, some day, come true. For her own sake, as well as Jim's, she had read and studied as much as she could of Alaskan conditions.

It was she who finally disclosed to Jim that the Russian seal-poachers were probably at fault in chasing him from his strike, and only wanted to get rid of the inconvenient witness. Thus she had reawakened the prospector's lagging interest in his find, but lacking the large store of capital necessary to exploit the mine, she could do nothing. Jim had used up all his savings in going from town to town trying to interest a big investor and had finally entered Owens' coal mine in order to get a little stake again.

Wizard Juneau was amazed at the extent of mining knowledge shown by this girl shipmate, and he had spent the greater part of the voyage from Sitka in imparting to her some of the secrets distilled from his long experience in frozen mining. He had brought on board the Bunting many of the publications of the U. S. Geological Survey, and of the Bureau of Mines, annotated by himself. He had brought, also, a number of crude maps of half-explored territory, either drawn by his own hand or by old prospectors, which maps and charts were among his most prized possessions.

"Some of these," he explained, "were made by Alf Brooks, one of the nerviest explorers that the U. S. ever sent out. I've been with him on more than one reconnoissance survey. And some were made by experts on the U. S. Revenue Cutter Bear. I sailed on her two seasons."

"And do you think, Mr. Juneau, that this island of Uncle Jim's is on the American side of the line?"

The "Wizard" pursed his lips with an expression of doubt.

"It's a toss of the dice," he said. "Ingalook, the easternmost of the Diomede Islands, where Jim found that piece of gold-bearing quartz, is sure American territory. I don't take kindly to Ingalook, though. There'd be trouble, there, in trying to install proper mining and crushing devices.

There's no landing place on that isolated granite dome standing forlornly out of the sea, except for seals, polar bears, or crazy prospectors like Jim, there.

"But this Chukalook Bank of the Road Agent's map, where the pay gravel and the lignite coal lie—supposing that it's the same as this little unnamed dot marked on the charts—seems to be right on the international boundary line. We'll have to wait until we get there to make accurate observations."

"Can you do that, too, Mr. Juneau?"

"Me? No! I can take a sight of course, but not accurate enough where it's a matter of minutes or even seconds of a degree. But Captain Robertson can. Like many of these amateur yachtsmen, he's a better navigator than the captain of some Atlantic liners. It's his hobby. Besides, he's got instruments of precision aboard that an admiral would envy. What's more, he's a certificated man, and his say-so on a nautical observation of longitude would be legal in the courts. Mine wouldn't."

"And suppose the island should prove to be on the Russian side?"

"Then, young lady, you'll have to turn Russian!"

"What nonsense! You know I wouldn't. No, but speaking seriously?"

"Well, seriously, then, you'd have to buy the island from the Bolsheviks, or from the Eastern Siberian Republic, or from the Japanese, or whoever happens to be claiming it. International rights up in the Asiatic Arctic are badly mixed up, these days. And that wouldn't be the worst of it. You'd have to pay stiff royalties and you wouldn't be sure of any sort of protection—unless it was the Japanese."

"We'll buy it, if we have to!" declared Jameine decidedly. "I'm not going to have anything happen that will spoil Uncle Jim's strike!"

"He's a regular dad to you, Miss Evans, eh?"

"He's the only one I ever remember," the girl replied. "My real father went up to Skagway, just a few weeks after I was born, only having stayed down in Montana long enough to see me. And, as you know, Mr. Juneau, he went over the Chilkoot Pass with Uncle Jim and never came back any more.

154

Mother died when I was quite small. I know Uncle Jim feels that 'Bull's little gal' is his own. I feel so, too!"

The grizzled mining engineer patted the hand with which the girl was holding open the chart.

"Don't ye worry," he said, kindly, "we'll make good. We'll bluff any one that comes to Chukalook — supposing we find it — long enough to get the best o' the pay gravel. If that don't do the trick, we'll fight.

"And there's another thing. If Chukalook doesn't pan out, there's the quartz at Ingalook. I've never seen the gold deposit yet — no matter how poor — that I couldn't turn into money, so long as I could get enough capital behind me to exploit it."

"Mr. Owens will give that," asserted Jameine confidently.

The "Wizard" shook a warning finger.

"Not just for sentiment, he won't," he said, "not if I read him right. He's generous enough, and he'd see that you and Jim didn't suffer. But he's too keen a business man to invest his money unless he sees a fair chance of return. We've got to show him!"

"He certainly doesn't seem as enthusiastic about it now, as he did when we started," Jameine agreed, thoughtfully.

"That's natural enough! Don't ye forget he's an Australian, and all the gold fields he's ever seen, there, and in South Africa, were in hot desert country. These waters don't look promising to him!"

The "Wizard" was right. Owens was scanning the slate-gray water flecked with foam and the sky of dripping fog with equal distrust and dislike. The pieces of ice-floe bobbing in the choppy current inspired him with uneasiness, even with fear. The assurances of his friend, the yachtsman, gave him no confidence.

Had it been possible, he would have been heartily glad to back out of his agreement, but there was no way he could do it with honor. He had sought out Jameine in Pittsburgh, had seen Jim's letters, and had checked up the Express Company's receipts of gold forwarded by the old prospector from the mining camps of Forty-Mile, of Circle, of Juneau, of Klondyke, of Dawson City and of Nome. Jameine's hopeful spirit and her determination to make good on Jim's strike had been infectious. Owens had set out, almost gaily. But this grim, inhospitable sea put a damper on his spirits.

"Doesn't the sun ever shine here, Jack?" he asked abruptly.

"Not often," was the yachtsman's cheerful answer. "That's why the fur seals love it. Why, bless you, on Pribilof Islands, where the seal rockeries lie, there aren't twenty days of sunshine in a year. I know these waters. I came hunting sea-otter once. We ran two summer months without seeing the sun."

"It's no place for me!" declared the mine-owner. "Those who like the sea can have it, and be welcome!"

The yachtsman bridled. He loved the sea.

"Open your nostrils, man, and sniff; that's pure air, at least. It isn't like what I smelt last time I visited your dirty old coal mine!" he retorted. "Every dog to its own kennel, Owens! After all, you wanted to come here."

Jim felt much the same way. Standing on the foc's'le head, the raw air, with its sudden hot spells when the sun gleamed dully through the fog, brought him welcome memories. It seemed homelike, after his brief experience in a coal mine. As he had said himself, he was a "sour-dough." The uncanny fascination that the Far North exerts on those who have once lived there, gripped him hard.

"Ain't no crowd here to worry a man!" he declared, drawing in deep breaths, "an' there's room enough to stand straight! Would you want to go back to them coal galleries, Clem, four feet high an' stinkin'?"

"They suited me all right before, Jim," the young fellow answered, "and I don't see why they shouldn't again. I got mightily interested in coal. Still, I needed a rest, and this trip is interesting, I'll allow. But wait till we get to the actual mining of the gold, and then I'll tell you which I like best."

"An' you, Anton?"

"I never want to go below ground again," the boy answered promptly. "But it must be awful cold here in winter—if this is summer!"

"Ay, it's cold an' dark, no sun at all for two months. An' a man'll go hungry often. But it's free an' open an' no one has a boss! What's more, there's gold!"

Anton shivered. The call of the North had not gripped him, yet.

Otto, beside the helmsman, was worrying him—neither with the weather, nor with the question of treasure. To the first he was indifferent, to the second he was satisfied with drawing full pay every day and not doing any hewing for it. With huge delight, he was absorbing all the superstitions of the sea, and giving the steersman a gruesome crop of tales of knockers and gas sprites underground.

There was no special reason why he should have come on the voyage, except that he had asked to come. Owing to Anton's hatred for coal mining—born of the entombment—Clem had used his position as Jim's "pardner" to bring the boy along. Otto, having taken what might be termed a paternal and prophetic interest in the imprisoned men, wanted to join the party.

Owens made no objection. He knew laborers would be wanted, and he preferred men who would not be likely to betray the secret of the gold. He knew the miner's unswerving loyalty, and was well aware that loyalty is the one quality which is beyond all price.

Towards the close of the afternoon, the Bunting shortened sail. They were drawing near.

Somewhere, not far from them, lay the Diomede Islands, those two great granite crags rising sheer out of the sea with deep water on every side. The lead would give no sign. There is no fog signal on the Diomedes. In such a thick and clammy mist as hung over the water, a ship could wreck herself upon those bleak coasts almost before she saw the surf under her bows. The wind was light, and the brigantine slid slowly over the water.

The "Arctic Wizard," his eyes accustomed to the northern skies, was the first to see a faint purplish blotch in the swirling mist.

"Land! Captain!" he warned, quickly. "Keep away! Keep well away!"

Almost instantly, the booming of breakers was heard.

Well was it for those on board that the Bunting was quick on her helm! She bore off, just in time, the creaming surf not more than three cables' length ahead.

"A little too close for my liking!" exclaimed the yachtsman, but treating the danger lightly. "That's Ingalook, I suppose, Mr. Juneau?"

"Ingalook she is. At least, I think so. I've never been quite so close, before."

"And I don't want to be, again! Well now, I suppose, the real treasure hunt begins."

He called Jim.

"How did you say Chukalook Bank bore from here?"

"From Chukalook," Jim answered, "on a clear day, I could see this island two points east o' south, an' the other island, the Russian one, three points west o' south."

The yachtsman looked at him thoughtfully.

"And there's no knowing what compass correction to allow for a pocket compass, and there's the magnetic variation besides. Well, we'll work it out! And how far away do you reckon the island was?"

"I don't know nothin' about sea distances, Cap'n. She looked just about the size o' my thumb-nail."

"So! How high was Chukalook Bank above the water?"

"She goes up like a wedge o' cake, Cap'n. Maybe five hundred feet at the highest point. Where I was workin' wasn't more'n fifty foot above sea level."

"Well," commented the yachtsman thoughtfully, "allowing for the curvature of the earth, and for low visibility on these seas that ought to make Chukalook about thirty or forty miles from here. We'll put on a little sail and cruise N. N. E. for a few hours."

But the bank was nearer than Jim supposed.

Shortly after dawn, a sailor posted in the cross-trees reported a flat berg to starboard. The sails were furled, and the Bunting came up to it slowly under her auxiliary screw.

Jim heard the engines and rushed up on deck.

"That's Chukalook!" he cried, after the first look. "Now, who says I'm dreamin'? Wait till I tell Bull's little gal!"

He had not long to wait.

The sound of excited voices on deck had awakened the girl, and she dressed and came up hastily.

"Jameine!" he shouted, as soon as she came up the companion ladder, "there's our gold!"

The girl ran lightly across the deck and pressed the old prospector's arm.

"I knew you'd find it, Uncle Jim," she rejoiced, "I said so, all along!" Then, turning to the mine-owner, who had also come on deck, she added, "There it is, Mr. Owens!"

The Australian looked. That low flat bank, slowly sloping upwards, fringed with ice and deep in snow, was none too reassuring.

"You're sure?" he asked suspiciously. "It looks to me a whole lot more like an iceberg than it does like a gold-field!"

The "Wizard" interrupted, fearing lest Jim should make some rough rejoinder.

"It looks like an easy landing-place and that's one good thing," he said, cheerfully. "The Captain, here, has been making soundings and says there is good holding ground."

"That's all I will say, though," put in the yachtsman. "It's not a harbor. You're exposed here to every wind that blows!"

"You mean I'd have to build a breakwater?" Owens queried.

"Probably, if you want smooth water for handling cargoes. But I doubt if you could manage it. The winter ice would chew your breakwater all to bits. There's five months of open water, anyway, and the summer months are not so stormy."

"I wouldn't try to build a breakwater!" Owens burst out. "How would I get men and materials up here?"

The "Wizard" winked at Jim, who was growing restive.

"Wait till we get Owens ashore and start on the gold," he whispered. "I've seen these backers get cold feet before, when they hit this northern country for the first time. They're the worst to hold back, often, after they once get going."

But Jim was thoroughly dissatisfied. There was more than a little likelihood that the old prospector would make some scornful remark, for he was in his own land now, and had all a "sour-dough's" contempt for a "tenderfoot." But Jameine's hand was on his arm and he obeyed the warning pressure.

The little motor-launch was lowered from the davits, with every member of the party aboard. None of the sailors was taken, for Jim did not want to run any risk of strangers taking up claims. The "Wizard" ran the engine, and the yachtsman took the helm.

One piece of mechanism, small but very heavy, was lowered into the boat. It sank her low in the water, but it belonged to the "Wizard" and he was not the kind of man whose acts any one would question. Picks, shovels, sledge-hammers, wedges, and dynamite were included in the cargo. Thus heavily loaded, the boat reached the shore, Jim pointing out the landing-place. It was not so easy to land as the Wizard had suggested. It was necessary to wade through the sponge-ice, churned up the shore, Jameine being carried in the huge arms of the, "Wizard."

The snow on the island was almost knee-deep, but, except Owens, none of the party minded. Jameine was the gayest of all.

"Lead on to the millions, Uncle Jim!" she cried.

But the old prospector made the girl take his arm.

"We'll git there fust, together!" he declared.

A few minutes tramping brought them to a depression in the snow.

"Here's the old glory-hole (an open pit, not a shaft), an' nobody's been here!" he announced triumphantly. He grabbed pickaxe and shovel and slithered in, with the confidence of a man who knew every inch of the ground.

A few scoops of the shovel cleared away the snow.

Below, though overgrown with dry weeds of many seasons' growing, were the infallible signs of human handiwork. Even the old sluice was there, though fallen to pieces.

The others crowded around the glory-hole. The moment of test had come.

"Here, 'Wizard'," said Jim, when he had exposed the workings, "there's where I was pannin' last. Jump in an' take a look."

The expert, despite his years, leaped in lightly. He took the pick from Jim's hand, and, with a few vigorous strokes, loosened some of the gravel. He scrutinized it carefully, first with the naked eye, and then with a strong pocket lens.

"Well?" asked Jim, impatiently.

"Where are the other prospects?" The "Wizard's" kindly tone had vanished. He was now a mining expert, at his work. Personalities had faded. Geological questions, only, had weight.

Silently Jim led him up the slope, Jameine and Clem following.

Despite the veiling snow, the old prospector located hole after hole with unfailing accuracy, until seven had been found and examined. The last one was half-way up the cliff.

At each prospect the "Wizard" loosened a small handful of gravel, examined it carefully and put it in a small buckskin bag, pencilling each bag in order. His expression changed not at all; he bore the true Western "poker face."

"What overlies this gravel?" he asked abruptly.

"Slate," said Jim.

"Let's see it!"

They climbed upwards.

On arriving at the stratum which lay above the gravel, dipping down at a sharp slope, the expert examined carefully the carbonaceous slate of which it was composed.

"We'll go back, now," he said at last.

But he expressed no opinion.

"What do you think of it, Mr. Juneau?" queried Owens, when the four climbers returned to the glory-hole. His tone seemed to suggest that he half hoped for an unfavorable answer.

"I'll tell you presently," was the non-committal answer.

Then he turned to the prospector.

"Show me that lignite outcrop, now!"

"Kick the snow away with your feet!" answered Jim, curtly.

Every one kicked vigorously. Under the snow was a thin layer of soil, and, below that, not more than two inches beneath the surface, was the brown-black gleam of a low-grade lignite. Owens broke off a piece from the outcrop and his expression cleared slightly. Certainly Jim's statement about the coal was justified, though it was of too low-grade a quality to be worth exportation; possibly his story about the gold might prove to be true, also.

Then the "Wizard," still without a word which might be construed either as hopeful or as discouraging, brought from the boat the heavy piece of machinery. He fitted it with a handle and bade Otto turn. The machine proved to be a small but very powerful crushing-mill, so devised that the hardest quartz could be ground to powder by hand. Besides which, it contained within itself, some modern devices for separating out the gold.

Bag after bag of the decisive seven was poured in, ground to dust, and passed through the separating riffles. Each of these riffles had a self-cleaning device. The expert weighed the gravel before grinding, weighed the scrapings of the riffles, and made careful notes on the results of each batch. All was done in utter silence.

Jim, the true prospector, who had often seen wealth or poverty decided by the twirl of a pan, stood immovable. If he were worried, he did not show it. Jameine, on the other hand, was trembling and white.

At last, the "Wizard," note-book in hand, turned to give his decision.

"Judging from a direct crushing and separating process, without the use of mercury," he said, "this gravel ought to give about six-dollars'-worth of gold to the ton. With mercury, perhaps two or three more dollars' worth can be extracted, and another couple of dollars by cyaniding. The gravel is soft and can be hydraulicked, during the summer. The gold is coarse and easy to separate. The quartz pebbles will yield more than enough to be worth crushing, but just how much is indeterminate.

"That's not rich! By itself, or in the interior, the deposit might not be worth working. But with lignite right on the ground, to make steam both for running the machinery and for steam thawing points, and with a pumping plant using heated sea water for hydraulicking, there ought to be a net profit of about three dollars a ton."

The news was received in silence, each voyager occupied with his own viewpoint of the decision.

Clem was the first to speak.

"We've come a long way to get three dollars!" said he, with an attempt at jocularity.

Anton grinned assent. Like Clem, he knew nothing about gold-mining.

Otto waited, well aware that the final result lay between Owens, Juneau and Jim.

It was Jameine, with her book-knowledge of mining, who put the vital question.

"How many tons do you estimate there may be in the deposit, Mr. Juneau?"

"Impossible to say, exactly, especially when the island is masked under snow. But the prospects have been carefully chosen. They suggest about four hundred thousand tons in sight, and probably a good deal more. The gravel is an early Tertiary deposit, lying between two beds of carbonaceous slate, the lower of which is lignitic. Judging from the strike of the beds, the gold-bearing gravel runs down under the sea."

"Then," said the girl, slowly, "if there are four hundred thousand tons in sight, which would yield a net profit of three dollars a ton, you figure on over a million dollars, clear?"

"If modern machinery is put in and the mine is run on a business basis, I should say at least that. Possibly more!"

There was a burst of excited exclamations from all sides.

Every one turned to Jim, who was looking out across the sea toward Alaska.

"Bull, old pardner," he said softly, "I reckon I've made good for your little gal!"

CHAPTER XII

A SIBERIAN FILIBUSTER

By July, Chukalook Bank was humming with noise. The clank of machinery, the pounding of stamp mills, and the grinding smash of giant jets of water driven from hydraulic nozzles, set vibrating the tiny islands on the borders of the Arctic Ocean.

The terns and gulls, driven from their century-old refuge, circled over the little spot of land with shrill cries and fled to nest on Ingalook; polar bears, who, in other seasons, had found a dinner of fat seal on Chukalook, swam toward the island from floating cakes of ice, and then retreated hurriedly; the sea otter, shyest of all the fur-bearing creatures of the world, sped to more isolated haunts.

The island itself was melting like a snowbank beneath a summer sun. A three-inch jet of water, immeasurably more powerful than the forceful spout that hisses from a fire-engine hose, roared vengefully night and day against the gravel bank, and ate away the hill.

The never-ceasing torrent of gravel and boulders, mingled with the water, rattled and rumbled downwards with the force of the current into a massive sluice. The bottom of this sluice was constructed of paving blocks, crossed with copper-plated riffles of tremendous strength, on which not less than two tons of mercury had been placed.

Thus considered, the installation of the Bull Mine—as Jim insisted that it should be called—was but a simple miners' sluice on an enormous scale. It was the same device as that which Jim's father and his partners were working on the Carson River when the Comstock Lode was discovered, save that the hydraulic jet performed all the work of digging and shoveling the pay dirt into the sluice.

Shortly before reaching the sea, however, the works became more complicated. The "Wizard" and Owens—one with Arctic and the other with Australian and South African experience—had arranged a system of separating the gold bearing gravel from the bowlders, and, later, the unproductive material from that which contained the precious metal. The smaller, gold-bearing part was washed into the stamp-mills, which worked incessantly, and which reduced pebbles and grit and sand and gold to a pasty slime. This, in turn, was led to cyanide tanks. Thus every particle of the gold was extracted.

Hydraulicking was not altogether new to Jim. He had seen it done on a giant scale, as in California during the seventies, when huge reservoirs and mile-long canals were built at a cost of many millions. Vast works these, belonging to a short and strange era of mining, immense constructions, now lying ruined and abandoned in the deserts of their own making.

That was before the farmers and fruit-growers of California had succeeded, in 1884, in securing the passage of a law to prevent "slicking," as hydraulicking was termed. It was time! Vast stretches of territory were being reduced to chaos by the appalling havoc which follows hydraulic operations on a large scale.

Many rivers were entirely choked by debris from the crumbled mountains and spread their waters in destructive floods. On one small stream alone, the Lower Yuba, over 16,000 acres of high-grade farm lands were reduced to a condition which an official investigator for the state declared "could not have been surpassed by tornado, flood, earthquake, and volcano combined."

Before the farmers had succeeded in stopping the hydraulic miners, a stretch of land, larger than all the territory devastated by the World War, was rendered a hideous desolation forever incapable of settlement. Ten years of hydraulicking had brought more than $150,000,000 in gold dust to the mining interests, but had caused a perpetual damage that ten times that sum could not repay.

In every civilized country, to-day, hydraulicking is forbidden, except on a small scale. It is only permitted in such cases and under such conditions that the mining company can dispose of the tailings without injury to property holders further down the stream.

The "gold ship" has taken the place of the hydraulic jet and the sluice. It is a weird device! It is nothing more or less than a dredge, floating in a lake of water—maybe in the middle of a desert—which, as it moves along, moves its own lake with it. It dredges, washes, and separates hundreds of tons of sand or gravel with the same water in which it floats, using the water over and over again. By law, the tailings which it leaves behind must be leveled, soil placed thereon and either grass or trees planted. Thus the gold ship advances over dry land, chewing its own way forward, and remaking the land it leaves behind.

On Chukalook Bank, however, hydraulicking was permissible. There were no farm lands to be spoiled. There were no rivers to be choked up. The tailings and the refuse could do no harm. On the contrary, by employing the forces of the current descending in the sluice, the "Wizard" operated a narrow-gauge tramway on an endless chain, and the tailings were emptied into cars which ran out to sea, making their own land as they went. The cars had a dumping device, and needed but one man to tip them. Thus little by little, a natural breakwater crept out seawards, forming a harbor in which ships could ride in safety.

As the "Wizard" had anticipated, Owens had become as enthusiastic after the value of the mine had been demonstrated as he had been coldly critical before. The lure of gold caught him anew, and he invested capital freely. He was an excellent business man and a good judge of men. Besides paying Juneau a large salary as superintendent and mine engineer, he had shrewdly put several shares of stock in the "Wizard's" name, thus ensuring his most hearty support.

Moreover, Owens had learned to appreciate Jameine. He had found out that the girl had taken courses in the business side of mine management as well as in the technical branches, and though her knowledge was theoretical only, it was sound. With her he could discuss detailed questions of book-keeping and the like, which only annoyed the mining expert. Accordingly, Owens appointed Jameine his personal representative, thus securing Jim's loyalty forever. This done, he returned to his coal mine in Ohio, leaving the "Wizard" in charge.

Otto had been made foreman, and, though he constantly related to the men under him how different were the ways of coal-mines, he was inordinately proud of his position. He was able to do that most important of all things in mine labor—to keep the workmen satisfied at their work without raising wages to the point where profit ceases.

Anton, despite his first objection to the country, had become a hero-worshipper of Jim. He had a new ambition. He desired, above all things, to reach the sublime height of being regarded as a "sour-dough." The boy had shown a certain natural quickness for mechanics, and, while on the yacht, had chummed up with the wireless operator of the Bunting. Capt. Robertson, on his second trip, had brought with him a small wireless outfit, which the operator installed on the highest point of Chukalook and taught Anton to handle.

Clem took the place of assistant to the "Wizard." His small knowledge of geology—though it was mainly of coal seams—was of service, and the young fellow was quick to learn. But the principal attraction to him, on the island, was "Bull's little gal."

Jim was the life and soul of the mine. He was here, there, and everywhere. The workmen, especially those who were "sour-doughs" themselves, found a keen pleasure in the thought that a man like themselves had thus made good. It fed the fuel of hope which flames so brilliantly in the Frozen North.

A typical gold prospector, all the complicated machinery of his own mine meant little to him. Jameine understood it all and did her best to explain it to him, but Jim could not be persuaded to take an interest in it.

One day he turned his back on the works. With pick, shovel, and pan, he set off to the other side of the island, where the little creek ran, and where he had first panned gold on Chukalook, before he began prospecting the gravel. Once more, from early morning to late evening, he dug and panned as of old. Each night he returned triumphantly with half a handful of gold dust as the fruit of his day's toil.

Jameine did not have the heart to point out to him that, with the Bull Mine running at full blast, his share of the profits brought him more wealth in an hour than did a week's laborious panning of the sands of the little creek.

168

She knew that Jim could have no greater happiness than, at the end of the day's work, to add a few more grains of gold dust to the growing heap that rested, in a bowl, openly exposed, on a rough table in her tiny sitting room.

But this peaceful exploitation of Chukalook was not to continue uninterruptedly.

One morning, the smoke of a good-sized steamer was seen on the horizon. She came, not from the direction of Ingalook, as the Bunting and the supply steamers came, but from the Russian island to the south-west.

Jim, busily panning on the creek, was the first to see her. He dropped his tools and hurried to the power house.

"There's trouble coming, 'Wizard'!" he said briefly, and pointed to the steamer.

"You mean she's Russian? It's likely enough, then," was the grave reply. "Though I don't know that they can do much."

"They chucked me off here, once!" the old prospector remarked, revengefully.

"They'll have their hands full doing it a second time! Counting all the workmen, we've a pretty strong gang here, Jim. And most of the men would fight."

The steamer drew nearer, and the mining expert went into the house for his field-glasses.

Presently she was close enough for the glass to reveal an unusually large number of men on her deck. There was a more sinister omen still—a six-inch gun in her bow!

"A converted cruiser! H'm, this looks serious, Jim! Send Anton here, on the run."

The boy came instantly.

The "Wizard" shot out his orders.

"Get to the mess-tent as quick as you know how and grab some food. Get a gun and some ammunition. Then climb up to the wireless station right away. If I blow one blast on the engine-house whistle, don't pay any attention. If there are two long blasts, you can come back. But if you hear a succession of short, sharp blasts, be sure you start sending, and keep on sending!"

Anton, keenly at attention, answered,

"What shall I send?"

"The S.O.S., first. Then the code signal for the Revenue Cutter Bear—you know it, don't you?"

"Yes."

"Then send—'Americans in peril, Chukalook' and give the latitude and longitude. You'll find that written down just inside the cover of the International Code Book. I put it there in case of need. Repeat the S.O.S., the code number and the message until you get a reply."

"And if I don't get a reply?"

"Keep on sending."

"Until when?"

"Until you're shot down, if necessary!"

"Very well, Mr. Juneau. You can count on me."

"I know I can, my boy. Now—hurry!"

The suspicious steamer came nearer and turned the corner of the newly made breakwater. As she dropped her anchor, she displayed the flag of the Eastern Siberian Republic, at that time in the hands of the Bolsheviks.

"We've some 'sour-doughs' in the plant," suggested Jim. "If there's goin' to be trouble, they'll be lookin' for front seats. Shall I get 'em here?"

"You might as well. They can bring their shooting-irons, too."

Jim was not long gone. When he returned, he brought ten men at his heels, all of the Roaring North breed. Most of them held posts of trust in some part of the Bull Mine plant and all were ready to stand by Jim through thick and thin.

The "Wizard's" address to the men was brief.

"Russian 'claim-jumpers,' I reckon," he said, pointing to the steamer. "If they're looking for trouble, they'll get it. We'll parley first, and if necessary, shoot afterwards. No one touches his gun till Jim fires. That's orders. Do you get it?"

The men nodded. Like most of their kind, they were chary of speech and the word "claim-jumper" means to a miner what the word "horse-thief" meant to the cowboy. There was no need to say more.

The men had gathered none too soon. A boat had put out from the steamer and was drawing close to shore. There were a dozen sailors aboard in a nondescript imitation of the Russian naval uniform, but armed with modern rifles. An officer was in the stern.

On reaching the landing-place, the officer leaped ashore, followed by the armed guard.

"Who owns this mine?" he demanded in good English.

"An American syndicate," the "Wizard" answered briefly.

"And who is in charge here?"

"I am."

"In that case, I am instructed to notify you that you are occupying Siberian territory."

"That," responded the "Wizard" curtly, "is either a geographical error or a deliberate lie."

The officer made a gesture towards his hip, evidently forgetting the sword at his side, a movement which both Jim and the "Wizard" noted.

"Sir!" he began.

"This island," the "Wizard" continued, ignoring the interruption, "is a few seconds more than forty minutes of a degree east of the international boundary. Observations of the most precise character have been taken by Captain Robertson of the Bunting and were duly recorded at Washington more than two months ago."

The officer seemed taken aback at this definite declaration, but maintained his position firmly.

"This is Siberian territory," he repeated. "I have orders to confiscate whatever gold may have been extracted, and to take possession of the plant, as it stands, in the name of my government."

"If you try it, you'll get shot," was the terse reply.

"You would fire on an officer of —"

Jim cut in, dryly.

"I'll fire on an American navy deserter, any time," he said, making a shrewd guess at the character of the intruder, "an' it won't worry my conscience none. What's more, I'll put a bullet through a claim-jumper, whenever I feel like it."

The self-styled Siberian felt that he was getting the worse of the argument, and his temper rose.

"Enough talk! I have received information that you are gold-mining on Eastern Siberian territory. You are hereby notified that the mine is confiscated. All those in authority will come aboard the cruiser Mir as prisoners. You will be taken to the mainland for trial. Perhaps you will have the opportunity to prove your observations as to longitude, there!" he sneered.

"Is the Eastern Siberian Republic at war with the United States?" queried the "Wizard" with dangerous quietness.

"That does not concern you! Deliver me, at once, the keys and working maps of the mine."

"No!"

Jim added a western retort that roused the deserter to a livid fury. He answered viciously,

"We've a six-inch gun aboard that can blow your works to splinters!"

"And then?"

"We'll come ashore and take possession. It won't do you any good to ask for mercy, then!"

The "Wizard" stepped forward, his giant frame towering above the intruder.

"This parley is over!" he thundered. "I declare you pirates, and give you five minutes to get yourselves off this island!

"Jim, get your watch out! If there's one of these scoundrels on shore at the end of that time, shoot! If any one of them makes a hostile move, shoot! And shoot to kill!"

He turned to the supposed Siberian.

"As for you, you'd better be the first one in the boat! Every one of these men is a two-gun man, and I reckon you know what that means!"

The officer stood his ground, and entered upon an argument as to the rights of the case, but was cut short by Jim's crisp announcement,

"One minute gone!"

For a second or two the filibusterer hesitated, but the odds were even, twelve against twelve. Well he knew that the Americans could shoot quicker and straighter than his men, who were an undisciplined lot. He realized, also, that he would be the first to fall.

Scowling, he gave the order to retreat, amid the open murmurs of his men, who, under Bolshevist rule, considered themselves the equals of their officers.

The instant that they were embarked, the "Wizard" turned to Jim.

"We haven't many minutes to lose! That hound will open up with the gun, as soon as he reports on board.

"Get to the house as quick as you can. Rush Miss Evans and all the office crowd into No. 2 gravel pit, pronto! Shells can't reach them there."

"I'll tell the engineer to whistle to Anton. Then I'll close down the works and get the men into shelter. But we've got to act lively!"

Crisply he gave his orders to the waiting men, several of whom were grumbling because they had not been allowed to "clean up the gang" as one of them phrased it. They brightened up, however, at the prospect that there would be a fight.

Half a minute later, the whistle sent out a succession of sharp blasts, and, almost simultaneously, there came the sharp crackle of wireless from the station on the hill.

A volume of Russian curses was heard coming over the water at this sound, and the rowers redoubled their efforts.

Presently, from all corners of the plant, the workers came hurrying. The last man was hardly down in the gravel pit when there came a detonation from the sea-front and a shell came whistling over.

It was not directed at the works, but at the tiny cabin on the top of the hill which held the wireless outfit. Fortunately, the cabin was partly sheltered by a rock, and, moreover, it was but a small mark to try to hit. Some twenty shells passed over the island or exploded idly on the hill before one struck the sheltering rock. The pieces screamed over the cabin, one fragment tearing a hole in the roof but doing no harm to Anton.

Truth to tell, the boy was thoroughly enjoying himself. He felt a hero. Never having seen a shot fired in earnest, he hardly realized what the effects of a shell-burst might be.

The wireless crackled on.

For two hours the bombardment continued, several pieces of shell having passed through the walls above his head. The rock protected the lower part of the cabin. Anton was crouched low over his instrument, and, as yet, the aerials were intact.

Then, suddenly, a piece of bursting shell whizzed across the wires.

Silence!

The wireless was down.

Chukalook Bank was absolutely cut off from all communication with the outside world. The men of Bull Mine must fight off the Siberian cruiser, alone.

The six-inch gun now was turned on the works, a nearer and an easier target. The power-house, the stamp-mills and the cyanide vats suffered most. A six-inch shell at close range can do an appalling amount of destruction. At the end of an hour, most of the works were in ruins. Yet shells could not destroy the gravel bank, nor damage the great sluice beyond repair.

The bombardment ceased for a few minutes.

Then four boat-loads of men put off from the cruiser, and, at the same time, the six-inch gun began anew, covering their advance.

"Let's get down to the shore an' keep 'em from landin'!" cried Jim.

But the "Wizard" held him back.

"And have our men killed for nothing? No, Jim, we've got a good trench here and can hold it. It'll cost them dear to attack."

"But they'll get all the gold from our last clean-up!"

"They won't, Uncle Jim," put in Jameine. "I opened the safe and we carried all the bags here."

"And your own little pile?"

The girl shook a little sewing-bag she was carrying, and laughed.

"I was sewing when you called me, and I only had time to throw it in here. Gold dust is all mixed up with pins and needles and things."

Jim nodded.

"You're right, 'Wizard'," he said. "This is the place we've got to hold."

"And we'd better fortify one end of it, solid, if the worst comes to the worst. Get some of the men to roll bowlders here to make a solid wall."

The boats drew up to the landing-place.

"Hand me one o' them rifles!" suggested one of the twelve men whom Jim had first chosen. "I'm good on the shoot. Them claim-jumpers is only about six hundred yards away. I can hit a runnin' rabbit, at that distance."

"Good enough," agreed the "Wizard," "if you can pot them off, so much the better. They began the trouble and they fired first. Are there any more snipers here?"

Two more of the men professed themselves to be fair shots.

Creeping out of the trench, the three snipers esconsced themselves in cover, leaving only a loophole for their rifles. Presently one, and then another rifle cracked.

Two of the invaders fell.

A volley followed. It pattered harmlessly against the bowlders where the snipers were hidden and passed high over the heads of the rest of the men, safe in the gravel-pit.

"This," said the first sniper, as he took aim and fired a second time, "is tame sport. It's too easy."

A third man fell.

The Siberians scattered. It was clear that they had little taste for this kind of thing. They found cover, and, for half an hour or more, not one showed himself.

Then a little group dashed across towards the house, evidently with the intention of pillage. The three snipers fired. One man fell, and two, evidently wounded, limped after their fellows.

Then, for hours, not a sign!

Evening drew down, a foggy evening, with a mist so dense that the faint gleam of what was almost the midnight sun failed to pierce it. By eleven o'clock, it was nearly dark.

"They'll attack around midnight, likely," one of the men suggested. "Can't we make a big fire, 'Wizard'?"

"There's no wood here, Bob," the expert replied. "As for the lignite, even if we could get enough of it here without exposing ourselves, it makes such a lot of smoke that it would help them more than it would us. No, we'll have to send out scouts, though it'll be dangerous for those who go. Who'll volunteer?"

A chorus answered him, the three snipers claiming the preference.

"No," said their leader, "I can't spare you. But I'll take old-timers, that's sure!" He chose them carefully. "Now," he said, when he sent them out, "keep your ears open. Don't shoot unless you have to. If you see or hear any one coming, get back as quick as you can. It's a risk, you know!"

"Aw, 'Wizard'!" exclaimed one of them reproachfully, "you ain't talkin' to tenderfeet!"

"If you were a tenderfoot I wouldn't have picked you for a man's job," the leader answered, knowing well the pride of the "sour-dough." "Out with you, now, and quietly!"

An hour passed, and then one of the scouts crawled back.

"They're comin', 'Wizard'!"

The other three scouts followed in short order. The Siberians were advancing in an extended line.

"To your places, men! Jim, you and the three I named will hold the breastwork. The girl's there!"

Jim looked longingly at the edge of the gravel pit, up which the men were creeping. He was torn between his desire to be in the forefront of the battle and his eagerness to be near enough to protect Jameine. But, like all men who have really known the life of the frontier, he obeyed a leader's orders unquestioningly.

A few minutes later, out from the half-gloom and the wet fog, an irregular line of fire ran, as a hundred or more rifles cracked simultaneously. The miners responded with a scattering fire.

The Siberians were on them!

The fog gave the attackers an advantage. The Americans had only the time to fire a second volley when the Siberians leaped over the edge of the gravel pit. A furious hand-to-hand conflict began, but the miners were terribly out-numbered.

Worse, infinitely worse, the attackers possessed those diabolical engines of destruction which were developed in the World War—hand grenades. These, thrown upon the frozen gravel, exploded in all directions. Into the disordered ranks of the miners, the Siberians charged with the bayonet.

Armed only with their rifles, which were useless at close range, and with six-shooters, a weapon of but short usefulness, the Americans fought a losing fight.

Yet they repulsed the first attack, but at a staggering loss. The "Wizard," seriously but not fatally wounded, was carried behind the breastwork, his last words before losing consciousness being an order to cover the shelter with flat slabs of slate, before the Siberians got near enough to throw their grenades into the little fortified space.

Jim straightened up.

"Good-bye, little gal, if I don't see you again!" he called. "My place is at the front, now!"

He assumed the lead.

A second attack, even more vicious than the first, followed. The miners had reloaded. Most of them had two guns, hastily snatched from dead or wounded comrades. But for the grenades, they could have more than held their own. It was not to be. When the second rush subsided, the Siberians held one end of the gravel pit. The farther end, where were Jameine and the wounded men, held firm.

There came a lull, and, from where they lurked, the defenders saw suddenly some flashes of light from around the wireless house.

"They're after Anton!" said Clem. "He's all alone, up there. We can't leave the kid!"

"Right!" agreed a couple of the men. "Let's go!"

But Jim stopped them.

"We're too few, as it is," he ordered. "Anton must take his chance. We've the girl here, the wounded, and the gold."

"He's my partner!" declared Clem, who knew the magic of the word on Jim.

"Me, too; I go!" declared Otto, in his most stubborn voice.

Jim hesitated. A partner's right was sacred.

"Go ahead, then," he said, "an' quick, afore the fog lifts. She's gettin' lighter, now!"

The odds were more even now. Between the barricade that the Siberians had thrown up hastily and the breastwork held by the miners, there was an open space, too wide for the throwing of the grenades. The six-shooters held it clear.

Again the Siberians rushed. Claim-jumpers they might be, but they were worthy fighters. They reached almost to the breastwork, and one man had his arm poised to throw a grenade within, when Jim leaped forward and brained him with the butt end of a pistol. For full ten minutes, it was a death-grapple, but the attackers were beaten back.

The case of the Americans was desperate. Ammunition was growing short.

Another such attack might finish them.

The Siberians, however, had suffered heavily, and, all unknowing that their foes were almost out of cartridges, refused to charge again.

The faint light strengthened. The mist began to rise. Soon it would be full daylight. The miners braced themselves for what they feared might be the last shock.

Jim, bleeding from two slight wounds, held his men well together.

There came a babble of voices and then a movement behind the barricade.

The Americans stiffened.

Suddenly, a sharp shot resounded across the water, followed by a second report, evidently from a gun of different calibre.

The Siberians clambered from behind their barricade and fled.

At almost the same instant, Otto, Clem, and Anton were seen to emerge from the wireless cabin, running down the hill and shouting. The boy had his arm in a bloody sling. So far as could be seen, the others were not hurt.

Jim scrambled to the edge of the gravel-pit and looked to sea.

There, her guns trained on the filibustering cruiser Mir, the Stars and Stripes flying at her stern, lay the U. S. Revenue Cutter Bear, summoned by the wireless messages of Anton, sent while the roof over his head was being rent by shell.

Jim's strike was not to go for nought. The gold of "Bull's little gal" had welded the partnership that a coal-mine disaster had begun.

THE END

Milton Keynes UK
Ingram Content Group UK Ltd.
UKHW010625250923
429338UK00004B/322